benben press

TRUTH AND LIES IN MURDER PARK

TIM MITCHELL is the author of *Sonic Transmission: Television, Tom Verlaine and Richard Hell* (2006), *Sedition and Alchemy: A Biography of John Cale* (2003) and *There's Something About Jonathan: Jonathan Richman and the Modern Lovers* (1999).

www.timmitchell.org.uk

Truth and Lies
IN MURDER PARK

a book about Mr Luke Haines

Tim Mitchell

benben press

this book is published by benben press

www.benbenpress.com

ISBN: 978-0-9556319-4-8

Printed and bound in
Great Britain by
the MPG Books Group

for my father

A few words from your editor

A writer approaches stately Eastworth Hall, home of the newly gentrified pop iconoclast Mr Luke Haines. Will he turn back? No, he keeps coming. He carries two suitcases. It is difficult to see the expression on his face from here. Ah. The camera zooms in. And out. And in. And out. A game is being played. But it is now clear that the expression is one of uncertainty.

The writer has come to the magnificent new country seat of Mr Haines, singer, song writer, 'Britpop progenitor', confrontationalist, in order to research a book on the great man. I do hope he has not packed any preconceptions in those bags. But I hope, too, that he has found room somewhere for his kid gloves. I happen to know that this writer is a lonely man. He has obviously chosen his profession well. He comes into Mr Haines's world alone. He will depart the same way. Lonely men, of course, are not much missed when they disappear. But there is a particular gap in this man's life, which lies at the heart of his loneliness. Will he find the means to fill it over these next few days? Will he find that human presence which he seeks, before he vanishes?

Well, having done the decent thing and accorded the writer an introduction, let us leave him briefly.

There. I have rendered him motionless. His leg is poised in mid-air. Ready to attempt another step, as soon as we need him. Let us now consider his subject.

What can we say about Mr Haines, who presumably sits or stands, or walks or lies somewhere within the walls of the Hall at this very moment?

Well, first let me follow the example of honest politicians the length and breadth of Britain and declare an interest. I believe that, from the Auteurs to Baader Meinhof, from Black Box Recorder to his solo work, he has been the most important artist to have operated in 'rock and roll' in the last fifteen years. So now you know where I stand.

Some observers, quaintly, have seen a contradiction in the reported recent 'nuptials' of this acerbic commentator, this patriotic dissenter, with a 'slumming heiress' in disguise whom – we are told – he encountered mere months ago in a bar in Las Vegas. Well, let us assume for a moment that these reports are true. In this case the observers' view of the story would fail to take into account the humanity and integrity that surely lie at its heart. For, after all, how would the philanthropic Artist, the true-Brit do-gooder revealed in this edifying tale, have known the secret identity of that ragged doll? The upright character conjured here was but reaching down into the gutter of modern America, pulling out a poor showgirl and showing her a glimpse of the stars. How was this fine figure to have known what has since been presented to us in these reports – that the young lady was apparently the main beneficiary of the will of the recently deceased James Jefferson Griff IV of Eastworth Hall, Surrey, and the inheritor of said house and its estate? When we read in these accounts of this 'Luke Haines' discovering that inside his 'new wife''s cracking cocoon of sequins and fake feathers there was actually a very butterfly in silk and lace, we feel, do we not, that his 'good luck' was no more than just reward for selfless generosity? The very best of British, I say, to the 'Lord Luke' of this story. Never was it so richly deserved.

Ah, the writer has resumed his progress. I must have leant on the 'play' button by mistake. Apologies. But now, almost immediately, he stops of his own accord. He puts down his suitcases. There are a couple of statues on the lawn in front of the Hall. He peruses them. Mr Haines himself installed them. They are somewhat out of character with the eighteenth-century architecture of the rest of the Hall, but that is all to the good. One portrays a young lady, one a young man. The writer reaches out and touches the statues. He strokes their legs. This is ill-advised. But, as we cannot stop him, we must let him do as he chooses. Let us avert our gaze and return to the more edifying figure of our real subject here.

Mr Haines's reputation will, of course, have preceded this tale. Which is obviously a good thing.

So is he, then, as we have all been led to believe, a contradictory man? Well, certainly – in fact his very oeuvre depends upon it. Is he confrontational? Yes. Is he a con man? Never. Is he, perhaps, a con artist? Well... an Artist is an Artist.

Mr Haines dares to be different. He is a man apart. He looks at the world from the sidelines – because from there he can see what is really happening. He sees things that others do not and reveals them in his songs. He is an outsider, a nationalist and a thinker. He is a saboteur, a monarchist and a revolutionary. A conservative and an anarchist. Another King Mob echo.

And, since early childhood – a revenge artist.

Ah, the writer has reached the foot of the steps to the Hall. Hah! See, he trips! He prevents himself from falling by plunging the cases down on to the stone in front of him. See now again – he kicks at the step on which he caught his foot. Careful, writer! That is nearly three hundred years old. Have some respect for the past. Mr Haines will not be happy.

The reports of Mr Haines's recent marriage were followed by a brief press statement from him:

'I'm rich. I made it. I'm retiring, Britain. Never work.'

Not quite what Guy Debord had in mind that day on the Rue de Mazarine, chalk in hand, but never mind.

After a decent pause (in deference, perhaps, to the memory

of JJGIV), there issued from behind the gates of Mr Haines's stately new abode – his Fonthill, his Neuschwanstein – a retrospective. Three CDs of the great man's greatest work in an exquisite boxed set. It was greedily grabbed by his adoring public. The collection was a summation of a career – but was it also an epitaph? Were the liner notes an obituary? It was, after all, entitled *Luke Haines is Dead*. And it was followed by silence. A nation caught its breath.

But no, Mr Haines was not dead. He was working in secret. There were precedents. What, after all, had Kurt Schwitters been up to, concealed even from his friends, in his house in Hanover? What had Duchamp created, hidden in the back room behind his 14th Street studio? And so, in the same spirit, we ask: Why has Mr Haines erected that giant cinema screen behind the locked doors of the old ballroom? And, while we're at it, what are those flashes of light out in the grounds, in the undergrowth, in the trees and in the sky?

Right, the writer has continued his lonely climb up the rock face. The stone lion at the top of the steps stares past him, not deigning to meet his gaze. The lion is guarding this domain. And he knows that the writer poses no threat.

Let us render the writer's movements into slow motion. There we are.

Ah, see how he inches upwards and forwards now, how his bags rise and fall like weights on a pulley.

Well, ladies and gentlemen, the time has nearly come. I can delay it only a little longer. It will soon be necessary to deliver you into the hands of this man. But have no fear, I shall not leave you alone with him. I will return at regular intervals – to interpret, to add and to correct.

As Bryan Forbes has noted, with regard to his film *Seance on a Wet Afternoon*, when one shoots a scene using two cameras, one cannot have two keylights, one cannot have two suns. I am the keylight, I am the sun.

Ah, the writer has reached his peak. He stands in front of the north entrance of the Hall. What awaits him inside?

A series of lessons. In history, politics and psychology. In respect, courage and representation. He will fail them. But then we knew he would. He has been selected. We hope that his failure, though, will be of interest. Shortly his hand will begin to rise. A finger will be released from it and will crawl through the air on its way towards the doorbell.

Right, before I take my temporary leave of you, I need briefly to explain what I have had to go through in order to bring you this book.

The editor's introduction to the book

I pride myself that I have managed to lick this writer's efforts into shape – that I have been able to make something worthwhile of a literary endeavour that was always going to be beyond its original author.

The writer's outpourings are presented here in the best light he could have asked for – the shadow cast by my own words. The story is that of Mr Haines's life and work – some actors will be along shortly to help us with the latter – but there is, of course, a minor sub-plot, too. And that is the slow vanishing of the writer.

Never let it be said that I have failed that man. I respect the sanctity of the written word – even when it is written by him. I respect – this is difficult for me to say – I respect what he wrote. So, no, I did not actually rewrite what I was given. But I have framed it. And a classy frame is a work of art in itself, is it not? And that is not all I did. I made annotations, too, in order to fill the many holes that I found in the text. You might say that I coloured in the background. I was forced, too, of course, to correct inaccuracies – to touch up the blemishes, as it were. But I do not call that rewriting. It was all part of my duty to the reader. Part of my job.

Oh, and I added an ending. Yes – I completed the writer's book for him. He was unable to do that for himself. He ran out of time. If I had not done this, all Mr Haines's efforts in getting him to the Hall – and keeping him there – would have been wasted. Not a word of thanks, though, have I received from the other side for my hard work! But then I suppose virtue is its own reward.

Ah, the writer is talking. Either that or he is eating. His jaw is moving slowly up and down. There is a figure in front of him, so it is a little hard to see. It is Mr Haines's butler! Welcome, Stevenson! And now we see the writer from behind. Yes, Stevenson is about to respond to his words – and now we see the writer from above. My word, the cutting on this sequence is sharp, fast and exquisite – and this is still in slow motion! I know – shall we speed the writer up? Rather a lot? Yes, I think we should. Right. Oh, there he goes, scuttling down the corridor like a berserk mechanical toy! No, not in there, writer! Ha ha ha – he's gone into the wrong room! Ha, ha! I say, this is fine entertainment. Ooh, he's out again. There he goes – into the Morning Room this time. Well done, writer! Look at his little legs blur!

What fun. Forgive me while I dry my eyes.

Right, I must say no more – for now. We have reached the end of our little introduction. I stretch out my hand – there – and press 'stop'. The writer vanishes. But what is that I hear? Is it a train pulling in at the station? Yes. It is nearly time, then, for the taxi driver to emerge from his place of concealment and to park up. And for our sub-plot to begin. There is someone on that train this driver must meet.

Right, here we go then. I speak with a heavy heart. Ladies and gentlemen, it is my duty finally to present to you: the writer.

Day One

I came down by train. Intercity to London. Crammed in with the long-distance commuters. Then a local down here. Stretching out after a handful of stops, feet up in an empty carriage. Then gliding to a halt on a deserted platform.

Nobody else got off at this station. The ticket office was empty. A metal sign swung in the wind. There was no one outside.

I stood there, suitcases in my hand, listening to the birds singing, staring at the sky. In the middle of nowhere.

It's a different world down here. Slower, quieter. It's like going back in time.

And then, down the approach road to the station, slowly, came a car. An old Cortina, grey and shiny, with a tiny black box on the roof, as if it was apologising for itself: 'TAXI'. It pulled up ten yards away from me, its bumper nudging the jagged white line of the cab rank. It sat there with its motor running.

I looked at the driver but he was just staring straight ahead of him. It looked as though he was waiting for someone. He hadn't even looked at me – but there was no one else.

I walked past the front of the car, looking at him through his windscreen, and stopped by his window. He didn't move. He was wearing a sheepskin coat. His head seemed to have sunk down into its collars. He was wearing dark glasses.

I was about to tap on the window when the glass began to

glide downwards and his head swivelled towards me. I bent down.

'All right, mate,' I said. 'Can you take me to Eastworth Hall?'

'I can,' he said.

'Stick these in the boot, shall I?' I asked, pointing to the suitcases.

He just smiled.

I walked round behind the car and stowed the cases. On the shelf inside the rear window, but facing towards the front, was one of those nodding dogs, a Great Dane.

I climbed into the back. There was a thick carpet and a smell of cigars. On the rear of the front seats were signs saying, 'Clients are politely requested to refrain from smoking.' It was clean and tidy inside.

We accelerated away. Looking into the rear-view mirror, I saw the Great Dane, front feet and arse planted like a tripod, begin to nod. I leant back into the seat.

'Are you staying long at the Hall, sir?' the driver asked as we turned left on to a country road, crows wheeling somewhere above, a curtain of trees on either side. I couldn't figure out his accent – it seemed to be a mixture of country yokel and something icier.

'I don't know really,' I said. 'I suppose it depends on Haines.'

He gave me a satisfied look in the mirror.

'Ah!' he said.

He looked right, left and right again – and then repeated the whole thing. Only after all that did we finally move off. The journey couldn't have taken more than ten minutes. Blurred hedgerows and fields. Deserted junctions. Not a single car.

It's a week since I agreed to do this book. I had to put the latest edition of the magazine to bed in a hurry. By the time I come back the printing will all have been done. It's my baby, that magazine, I do everything myself. British guitar bands, now and then, is what I write about. Anything with bite and a heart. I live alone and I work alone. I'm off to stay at Haines's place and interview him. He rang me out of the blue.

'Wanna write a book about me?' he said. 'I've got a publisher. You've done your little pamphlets on those other talentless wankers. This'll be a step up for you.'

I've never really got into Haines's stuff, never paid it much attention. It's all right, though – I'm catching up. The book's in safe hands.

We stopped on a bend in the road. Underneath a giant arch. I got my cases out of the boot – the driver just sat there.

No chance of a tip then. Lack of service included, mate.

He slammed the car into gear and pulled away, wheels flying, without even winding the window up. I took a step back. When he turned right just before the next corner he hammered it round without even a look.

This isn't the kind of place you'd get to by public transport. It's not on a bus route. After the dust had settled, I was left, with a suitcase on either side, staring up at that huge stone archway.

It's bigger than the bingo hall in the high street. And there's no steady stream of people trotting past here. No neon lights or graffiti scrawls, no notice board on the ground outside, chained to the wall. Nothing like that. No sign of time ever having passed since this thing was built. It's made of solid stone but there are windows in it – it's like someone lives in it. There's a wall either side, with high iron gates blocking it. Through the gates you can see a rust-coloured road that runs away into the estate before curving out of sight. And either side of that there are green fields. There's a buzzer on the gates – a little silver box with a silver button. I pushed it.

The gates opened straight away. No buzz from an intercom, no fumbling followed by a far-off voice asking who I was. I slipped through quickly. The lift doors back home shut on you halfway.

The gates didn't make a sound. But then everything is quiet round here. Which means you can hear the little things. Things you can't see. Standing here, it was crickets, jumping in their little jungle either side of me.

I started walking. Down the yellow brick road. As I carried on, though, and the fields seemed to grow and stretch, I was thinking of that scene in *North by Northwest*, when the crop-sprayer comes. And there was another thing, too, that came into my mind – the image of Robert Johnson walking along a dirt track towards the Crossroads. But I kept going, and no Tin Man came and no plane and no Devil. Then the road made that bend and I followed it – and there it was. The house.

It's not a house, it's a mansion.

No, it's not even a mansion. It's a palace, carved out of cream stone.

The photos give you no idea. It's wide as a harbour and tall as a cathedral. The central part is like a temple, with marble and pillars, then it curves round on either side through granite walls with rows of windows and battlements to huge wings, lined with more pillars. So many windows. How many rooms has it got? You could keep an army inside this place. Lined inside the walls of the halls, fingers to their lips, holding their breath. As I walked towards it, it got bigger still. Blowing up in front of me like a zeppelin pumped full of gas.

On the left there's a lawn the size of a cricket pitch and behind that there's just fields, as far as you can see. Between the lawn and the house there's another lawn – and two big statues. From behind, walking towards them, all you can tell is that one is a man, the other a woman.

Once I was standing, though, with the house filling the sky in front of me, I turned back to face them. The woman is Vanessa Paradis – Haines once asked her to duet with him on one of his tunes. The man is 'Lenny Valentino' from Haines's song of the same name – the dying Lenny Bruce inhabiting Rudolph Valentino's dead body. Paradis looks starstruck. Valentino's lips are closed but through them Bruce silently screams.

The second lawn, between the house and the statues, is the shape of a half-moon. There's a path that goes straight across it to the wide stone steps, worn smooth in the middle, that lead to the front door.

As you get closer you can see that the paintwork at the bottom of the doors is blistered. Years of blows from boots and baggage. And then, when you get to the top step, you see that the copper doorknobs are both dented, crumpling inwards in pockets like craters on tiny moons.

I stopped in front of the doors and looked up. Set inside a stone canopy there's a pair of windows. There was a glow from inside the glass, like orange embers. Higher up, in a pink-marble alcove, there's a bust of a man wearing a wig. The eyes were angled so far down towards me – just a glimpse of pupil visible – that it looked as though they were trying to disappear inside their own sockets. They had a fierce look.

I was about to reach out to press the bell when one of the doorknobs started to turn by itself. And then the door opened and there was a guy in a suit and a black tie standing there. With his collars sticking up.

What's going on here? I thought. That idiot of a taxi driver must have brought me to the wrong place. This must be Lord somebody. He's going to point a gun at me or set his dogs on me or aim a kick at my shins or something. But then he started talking, and he was calling me 'Sir'. I couldn't figure out what he was going on about but then he mentioned 'Mr Haines' and I noticed he was wearing tails. He was the butler. Haines has a butler. He's in his fifties, I'd say, but obviously looks after himself – there's no fat on him but plenty of muscle. And then my eyes flicked back up to that bust. It was Haines up there. Like some aristocratic gargoyle, warding off evil spirits. But then the butler moved aside. He was making way for me, inviting me in.

And then I was inside the hall.

It's like being inside a giant bell – it even rings like one. The sound of the door closing swells around it, filling its space, and then falls away again, collapsing on to the blue and white stone floor.

The walls are lined with long tapestries in crimson and faded yellow, and big oil paintings. In one of the paintings there's a man who looks like Charles I. The rest are red-faced no-necked men and white-skinned long-necked women. In one there's a fat man in a fancy uniform standing next to a black dog. The walls go up and up and then on the ceiling there's a dome. It's all white at the top, apart from a band of gold. The yellow embers I saw in the windows are tiny bulbs set in glass chandeliers.

The butler had vanished. To the left and the right of the hall there are openings into dark corridors. He must have disappeared when I was looking up at the ceiling. I didn't even hear him go.

And then he came back. Walking fast towards me from the right, emerging out of the gloom. No noise, though, from his feet on the marble floor – silent soles. He had a serious look on his face. Maybe it was all the over-the-top stuff everywhere in this crazy place but I suddenly thought, 'Maybe Haines has croaked. On the throne, like Elvis.' But then the butler said, 'Mr Haines would like you to follow me, sir,' and we were off down the gloomy corridor, all wooden panels, waxed floorboards and dark ceilings. The sound is boxed in, your footsteps come right back at you.

There's a staircase off to the right, but it twists straight away and you can't see where it goes. Then there's a door on the left with a gold handle and rosewood panelling – it was closed – but we kept going past that and then there was a whiff of floor polish as the butler reached for a handle.

The door opened, and widened, and spread into a huge room, full of light, with windows up to the sky. They look out on to the grounds on the south side of the Hall. What you see through them would fill your dreams for weeks.

There's a lawn out there the size of a field, and it's bordered by woods. It's flat and empty and rolls gently down towards a lake that's like a three-panelled mirror. First you see bushes there, then sky, then trees. The other side of the lake, real fields roll up and up, bordered by narrowing elms, and rippling like waves until they dissolve into oak trees that rise to meet the sky. Right ahead, embedded between the oaks in the far distance, like the prize jewel in a shop window, is an arch like the one I walked through to get here. It's like the gateway to an invisible horizon. Your eyes go straight to it and they stay there.

The butler said something to me but I was too wrapped up in the view to take it in. He must have disappeared again. By then I was walking towards the windows and staring out. My mouth was probably sagging open. It's the scale that gets you.

And the perfection. Perfection on such a scale.

It's all framed in the tallest windows you've ever seen. Built not just to show you all of this but so you can see it in the context of the sky, too. As if that's the company it deserves to keep – as if it belongs with the gods.

Behind me I heard the door opening. This time I heard footsteps coming towards me – a woman's heels. I turned round. A brown-haired girl in a blue uniform with a white cap carrying a silver tray with a teapot the size of a watering can. She put the tray down on the table and said, 'Thank you, sir.' Then she did a little curtsy. Her earrings were tiny golden hearts. She turned round and started walking out again. I said, 'What's your name, love?' but she just carried on walking as if she hadn't heard me.

I poured some tea from the watering can into a tiny white cup with a fancy handle you could barely get a finger into. Then I sat at the table and looked out at that view and thought, 'I could get used to this.'

Actually there are three windows in there. I was looking out of the middle one. They've all got window seats – wide and deep enough that you can almost lie on them. Up at the top of the windows, locked into tiny wheels in the frames, thin ropes fall down towards the floor.

The tea was a funny colour, it was some weird shit, but I was thirsty so I drank it.

Aristocracy and rock and roll don't mix. Look at Jagger and Ferry. And you can't do it the other way round – you can't start off an aristo and then make yourself cool. It never works. That's one thing inherited wealth can't buy you – attitude. So they go for what they can, those guys – they sell their celebrity snaps, race grand prix cars, slum it with glamour models. Lord Lucan came closest. Boozing and gambling instead of working, and then running from the law – Haines is an admirer. Maybe Lucan was innocent. Maybe the fact that no one believed him about what happened that night set him free. Perhaps he took his chance to swap his life for another one.

Maybe Haines is going to be the one to make the aristo thing work? You'd have to love it and despise it at the same time –

he could probably manage that.

I was in that room until it got dark. Haines never showed. Most of the time I was just sitting on the window seat looking out at all that tranquil madness, trying to get my head round it. I imagined bringing Fiona here, showing her all this. But she's gone – and it's better that way. Every so often I got up and stretched my legs. It's big and empty, that room. Just that low table and some creepy portraits on the walls. A porcelain woman with a Pekingese. Another fat man with a hat and a sword. The sound bounced around the walls when I walked. It was like being in an art gallery. I poked my head out of the door a couple of times, and stared into the darkness at the ends of the corridor, but there were no signs of life. Back to the window. I never saw a soul out there. It was like it was all mine.

'My little place in the country,' Haines had called it when I spoke to him.

I read the newspapers when they announced the marriage, I saw the photo spreads. They were just library photos, though – Haines wouldn't let anyone in here to take new ones. But like I said the photos give you no idea of what it's like to actually be here. How can a two-dimensional photograph that's been framed and scissored – or even a few of them – convey this? This is bliss. Utopia. Paradise.

'You'll have to tell the truth,' Haines said on the phone. And then he said – in a soft hiss – 'We'll make it an authorised biography.' Here's a golden thread, he was saying, but don't pull too tight or it'll snap.

Then he told me he didn't want me talking to anyone else or wandering about looking for people or stories.

'No sniffing around,' he said, 'no poking your nose in. No rooting through the ground looking for truffles.'

He needn't have bothered. I'll do what I always do. I'll search for the soul of the songs. For the soul of their writer.

'Come down for a few days and have a chat,' he said. 'You can sleep on the couch.'

Sure, I thought. I'll come.

It was uncomfortable squeezed up in that window seat, my

arse numb, my neck stiff and my back sore but I didn't want to move. I was watching the sky fade as if someone was gradually turning down the brightness on a television screen that filled the horizon. I was watching night fall exactly the way someone would have seen it happen three hundred years ago.

And then the butler came back. He just appeared. Maybe I'd dropped off for a minute or two. I thought he was going to have a go at me for sitting on the window seat with my feet up. He did give me an odd look – sort of up and down, a bit condescending – but he didn't mention it.

'Mr Haines would like me to show you to your room now, sir,' he said. 'After you have settled in and freshened up, he would be grateful if you would join him for supper in the dining hall.'

My own room. I hadn't expected that. I climbed out of the window seat and stretched.

I had a little chat with the butler on the way up. He walked in front of me and hurled his words up to the ceiling. I think he's probably all right. Not as pompous as he sounds. He started working here when Haines moved in, apparently. I asked him his name.

'Mr Haines has taken to calling me Stevenson, sir. A little private joke of his. It has stuck, you might say.'

'Does it run in the family, the... butler stuff?' I asked.

'Butlering was the occupation of both my father and my grandfather. There are few of us left these days. I consider it an honour, but I look forward, too, to the day when my job is finally done.'

Odd to find someone who still thinks of their work as a calling.

There was a thick darkness in that corridor – it was like looking down a well. We went past the dining hall on the left. A double door there was open. I could see long wooden tables and more tall windows, flashing black in the night. I stopped for a second and looked inside. More oil paintings on the walls – in the moonlight I could make out a man in uniform with his arm on a horse's neck, a man with a swollen chest, wearing a wig. And then on the right I heard sounds of banging, and then there was another, smaller open doorway and a man in a white uniform with a string around the middle and a chef's hat, beating a big aluminium pan.

'I'm a vegetarian, Mr Stevenson,' I said as we walked on. 'Is that going to be a problem? Because if so...'

'Please call me Stevenson, sir. You're a vegetarian. Mr Haines did not mention that. Perhaps he could not bring himself to. He is particularly fond of meat – in fact he prefers it bloody. He once told me that if an animal has fulfilled its role in the scheme of things by dying for one, then one should attempt to eat it in a form as close to its natural state as possible. Well, I'm sure we'll be able to find you something suitably anaemic for now, sir. And who knows what the future may bring.'

We had come to the end of the corridor. We were talking in front of a white door, inlaid with gold-etched panels. Stevenson turned and pushed it. And then we were at the bottom of a narrow, winding, stone staircase, carpeted in cream, with gold stair-rods. I looked up. It seemed to climb forever, twisting and narrowing like a corkscrew.

We stepped on to it and as soon as the door shut behind us and the sound funnelled up and vanished, it was silent inside. As if it was sealed off from the rest of the building. Even the banging from the kitchen had gone.

We began to climb. It was like falling up. I put my hand out to the wall. There were tiny bumps and swellings below the white paint.

And then, for some reason, I felt as though I was inside a crematorium. As if I was walking up to meet a ghost that was rising out of the ashes into the sky.

Halfway up we stopped. I followed Stevenson into an opening in the wall, a cutaway doorway. Inside were two rooms, carved out of the stone. One of them's my own bathroom – it's through the door on the left. Then we were walking down a step into the bedroom.

'You'll be comfortable in here, sir,' said Stevenson.

There's a window at the far end of my room. Even standing by the door you can see across the front lawn to the fields behind, and up to the clouds above, with everything framed narrowly in the glass. It's like looking down a corridor to the sky.

There's a thick red carpet in here. My suitcases are on the floor next to the bed. The bed has the sheets and blankets turned over so they creep over the edge.

I walked over to the window. To the right you can see the east end of the Hall – where it curves out into a colonnade with a balustrade on top. The pillars along the colonnade look bunched up from here, crammed together like the party faithful at an old-time political meeting. Further round, there was something I hadn't noticed before – another arch. Another gateway.

Stevenson had vanished again.

There's a desk in here. It's got a pile of paper on it, a bottle of ink and a fountain pen. I doubt I'll use any of it, though. I do all my writing on the laptop. I unpacked it and plugged it in. It was good to see the old desktop materialising. My life's inside that computer. All the issues of the magazine, all my emails. Letters to Fiona. And now there's folders with Haines's interviews and music press articles and lyrics. MP3s of all the albums and the singles – and the bootlegs and the sessions. There's always people who have got all that stuff. Believers. It's easy to track them down. I've gathered everything together, I'm doing the research. It's all there.

Not long after I'd finished writing all this tonight, Stevenson came back. I'd left the door open. I looked up and there he was, standing to attention.

'Dinner is served, sir,' he said.

And then he added, looking down at me:

'We usually ring a bell.'

I followed him down. Very straight-backed, Stevenson is. He started the conversation himself this time. And now his voice boomed and ballooned around us before vanishing up the staircase. Haines couldn't make it, after all, he told me. He sent his apologies.

'So I am afraid you'll have to dine alone, sir,' Stevenson said. 'The maid will serve you.'

The dining hall is big enough to seat that invisible army, but I was all on my own. It's long and high and white. Another of those gold bands goes round it at head height. The dark tables – there are about twenty of them – are laid out like a phalanx. I'd been put on a table at the end of the hall nearest to my staircase. The rest of the room stretches away in front of me. I can look out of the window to my right and towards the door to my left.

All those empty tables and chairs, in that unfilled room. Oil paintings and gold paint on the walls. Ancient wood and stone. Being waited on.

It's just me at home so I do everything myself. That's how I like it. Even when Fiona was round, I wouldn't let her do anything.

I can see different paintings from here. There's one of a family group. A thin servant kneels, looking up at a small boy who's on the chunky side and standing on a chair. The boy's dad is tying a cravat round his son's neck while his mother stares at the kid like she never wants to let him go.

I was served by the same maid who had brought me the tea. The food was egg, tomatoes, mushrooms and sauté potatoes, with a green salad. It was excellent.

There are three sets of tall windows spaced out along the wall of the dining hall. But it was all just black outside. No light from out there, just reflections in the glass from the chandeliers. Like luminous sea creatures, floating deep in the water. There could have been anyone out there. Down on the lake, maybe, in a rowing boat, staring up at the house. You'd never know. The dining room would be lit up for them, like a window display in a department store. Like Christmas lights.

I wonder how long I'll be here? One good interview session with Haines, maybe two, and I'll be on my way.

After supper, back in my room, lying on my bed. It couldn't be less like my room back home. No broken springs in the mattress. No damp patch on the ceiling or sickly wallpaper bubbling on the walls. No trapped air in the pipes banging to be let out whenever anyone has a bath or a shower or flushes the toilet or washes their hands or boils a kettle or has a drink. No landlord's son to come barging in for the rent, gun tucked inside his jacket, at seven on a Sunday morning. The magazine's doing well but I can't afford to move out just yet. A couple more decent issues and I'll be on the way. Down by the river would be nice. It's quiet down there.

Why did Haines choose me for this? He could have got anyone to write a book, now that he's famous. He must have read the magazine, must know I'm no music-biz ponce. He must know I'll tell it how it is.

I forced myself to sit down in front of the laptop again for a bit, making some notes, but I couldn't get a hold on my thoughts. I want to see the rest of this place, I want to explore.

I went out on to the stairs again and stood there for a minute. Not a sound. I closed my eyes. I imagined that after the old boys who built this place died, no one took their place. I imagined that it had been empty and silent like this ever since.

I started climbing the steps, in bare feet. Two at a time, stretching out. There's a thin carpet on the staircase – you can feel the firmness of the stone through it. Soon I was at the top. The light was dim – just a gentle glow coming from a wall lamp high up in the corridor to my right. I walked towards it. The carpet here was almost bare – rougher, too, worn down to its roots. On the left was an open door. I walked in. In the darkness I could make out the outline of a bath. I turned on the light.

Another bathroom – but nothing like the one downstairs. Mine's got a tiled floor, this is just stone. Mine has matching tiles on the walls, but this is just plaster, and it's cracked and crumbling. My bath's spotless, shiny and fitted. This one's got a big stain scorched into the enamel below the hot tap and another, smaller one by the plughole. It's just a big tub on legs. There's a mat hanging over the side – grey and shabby. At the far end of the room there's a small window, square and frosted, its frame blackened by mould.

Out in the corridor again I found five or six more rooms. The door of one was ajar. I pushed it open. The lamp in the corridor is directly opposite. It was shining like a moon right into the room.

Inside it was like a bedsit in an old-fashioned boarding house: a solid chest of drawers with an old-fashioned razor, a shaving brush and a white bowl, a dark wardrobe – no mirror – hulking in a corner. Stark, bare walls. A single bed, with the cover drawn up over the pillow and neatly folded behind it. In the corner there was a wooden chair, its back flat and straight. The room had an odd smell, too, a mixture of things: aftershave, shoe polish – the old stuff you get in a tin – and disinfectant, all mashed together. It felt cold in there, colder than in the corridor or in the bathroom. The ceiling drops down at the far end of the room. It's like an attic room.

I went out again, back along the passageway and down the staircase. But I kept going past my room, down the spiral stairs to the bottom.

The spring of the door down there was tight and it opened slowly.

The corridor looked empty but it was hard to tell because it was so dark – I couldn't even see halfway down it. There was no sound from the kitchens. I moved out. The door squeezed shut behind me like an airlock. I started walking down the corridor, aiming for a pale light I could make out now down at the far end. As I passed the kitchen, though, suddenly it was as if an electric storm had struck. Lights flashed, sputtered – and then beamed on full, burning bright. I shielded my eyes and lowered my head. A horde of cockroaches were stampeding for the gloom below the stove, fridges and kitchen units. The patter of a thousand tiny feet. I looked up again. Ahead of me in the corridor, his finger on the switch, was Stevenson.

'May I help you, sir?' he asked.

The light. The sight of Stevenson. The sound of his voice. I could barely think.

'I was just going to stretch my legs a bit,' I managed to mumble. 'Bit of exercise before I get some kip.'

'Mr Haines advises against that kind of thing, sir,' Stevenson replied slowly. 'Particularly at night. And when one is unfamiliar with the layout of the grounds. There are sudden gradients and tight corners. Obstacles. It really can be quite dangerous. I'm sure he would be happy to show you around in the morning, sir. As I said, he does apologise for his absence today.'

'Sure,' I said, 'No problem. I'll get an early night. I'm a bit knackered anyway. After the journey. Night.'

'Good night, sir,' he replied in an even voice and didn't move. I turned round.

Upstairs I sat in front of the laptop again for a while, making more notes. I've already done some background reading – as well as the interviews and articles. When Haines mentions something in songs or interviews, I check it out. I've done the Baader-Meinhof gang, I've read *Brighton Rock*, David Peace's *1974*. I've brought Robert Irwin's *Satan Wants Me*, too – there's a Haines song based on it. Bollocks. I was going to bring the DVD with me – *Seance on a Wet Afternoon*. Shit. I know exactly where I left it. It's sitting on the bottom shelf by the photo of Jessica and me on Brighton Pier.

Stevenson's like the Comte de Saint Germain – vanishing into thin air and materialising again at will.

Editor's note—

Right. I am back, ladies and gentleman. I hope my absence has not been too much of an ordeal.

It will be necessary to conclude each of these pieces of writerly guff with a commentary. They cannot be allowed to stand on their own. There is so much to be added and amended. Objective truth is a nebulous concept but we must pursue it as assiduously as possible.

Very well, then, let us return once more to the writer's arrival on our scene.

During his taxi ride to the Hall, the writer discovers what he regards as contradictory elements within the accent of the driver. Of course, there could be all manner of explanations for this. The writer, though, seems uninterested in considering them. This is an early disappointment for us – but we will have to learn to live with being let down.

The taxi driver, having left the writer at the arch, pulls up around the corner. Cut to a close-up of him reaching up to his neck. His hand takes hold of the caul – the underpart of his wig – and reveals a bare head. The double meaning in this action is apparent. The taxi driver is symbolically removing that other caul – the portion of the amnion sometimes found upon the child's head at birth – from the writer he has just delivered to Mr Haines. This sequence echoes the scene in *Seance on a Wet Afternoon* when Billy the kidnapper returns to Myra with the child she desires. We see a hand, sealed inside a doctor's transparent rubber glove which is seemingly festooned with blood and mucus, reach up into the air. Myra hands Billy a towel – and he uses it to mop up what is in fact hair dye streaming from his head.

So, the writer's magazine is his baby. Well, if so, it must be the tiny spawn of a witch. It has, by his own admission, completely neglected the UNRIVALLED GENIUS OF MR HAINES. Do not worry, he will pay.

The writer assures us that this book is in safe hands. I make the same assurance. But, unlike him, I have the power to deliver on it.

Elvis and Robert Johnson? Does the writer expect us to take this stuff seriously? This is the south of England not the deep south of the USA. Mind you, an image that I have just conjured up – of Mr Haines gorging himself on venison burgers while the Devil appears in front of the writer – is a pleasing one.

The writer fails to hear what Stevenson says – both at the north entrance and again as he stares out through the windows of the Morning Room. He really should pay more attention. Fortunately for him Stevenson was merely extending a welcome from Mr Haines and then delivering a few further pleasantries regarding the writer's comfort during his stay. Exceeding his job description there, I would say, but never mind. Stevenson is a good butler but he is also a human being. He deserves more respect from the writer.

Lord Lucan innocent? What is the writer thinking? What is he trying to say – that the butler did it? But yes, his lordship obviously is still alive in the middle of some undiscovered

Peruvian jungle, worshipped by the tribespeople as he sits atop a throne of Inca gold.

Fiona? What is this – a lost lover? The writer is right to shove her into the past. Do that with everything else, too, is my advice to him. Put your affairs in order, sir!

'It was like it was all mine.' In your dreams, matey! We should remember that even Mr Haines himself is not the legal owner of this place. The young lady who is, though, has been happy to allow him to take charge of it and to dictate what goes on within its grounds. She has urged him to regard it as his own and to do with it what he wills. It is, therefore, his dominion.

Bliss? Utopia? Heaven? No, this is Arcadia.

The writer wants to find Mr Haines's soul, does he? Well, one should always be careful what one wishes for.

Right, where is my guide book? Ah, here it is.

The 'bloke who looks like Charles I' is Sir Richard, the Viscount – a secret Royalist under Cromwell (his wife wore his miniature beneath her dress – and above her heart – whenever he was away) who flowered after the Restoration. He rebuilt the existing Hall from scratch – and then spent twelve years constructing gardens here in the French style. They were later destroyed by the first Earl, who built some English ones – which are still there. A lesson to us all, I think. The Viscount started the ball rolling – partly by marrying well. So important, of course. He then spawned the Marquess.

The Marquess is conspicuous by his absence amongst this company. He resigned as President of the Board of Trade on his marriage to a highly pecunious widow and immediately began to deepen his interest in freemasonry. The temples in the grounds of the Hall were built by him. There were problems after he wrote and privately published an injudicious book on the funny apron fraternity, detailing arcane procedures and naming those who took part in them. His portrait was removed from the North Hall after his death and stored in an attic. Mr Haines recovered it from there himself and it now hangs in his private quarters.

The 'fat man in the fancy uniform' is the first Earl. He was a queer sort. He is wearing the robes of the Order of the Garter. *Honi soit qui mal y pense.*

The black dog is Marmaduke, the first Earl's labrador. This dog was this man's best friend.

The 'porcelain woman with a Pekingese' is the wife of the first Earl, with Ermintrude. She suffered by the Earl. The Duchess that is, not the pooch. Her husband, as we have just noted, was a dog lover. Holding his nose one night he somehow managed to impregnate her with the seed of the second Earl. His wife – not the bitch.

The man with his 'arm on the neck of a horse' (the description is not strictly accurate but I'll go with it) is the first Earl once again. Clearly it was not just dogs whose company he enjoyed.

Right, the 'family group'. It is the first Earl, his wife and son – the infant second Earl. Hmm. Even at this early stage in his son's development, the first Earl has a slightly troubled expression. He obviously knows the kid's going to turn out bad.

The 'man with a swollen chest, wearing a wig' is the second Earl as a young man – the swelling of the chest came early on, that of the stomach developed a little later. His wife and daughter appear beside him. Each suffered by him.

The 'fat man with a hat and sword' is the fully mature second Earl. He had a cannon which he stationed on the lawn outside the north entrance of the Hall. A powder monkey from the scullery heaved giant balls into the gun's mouth, from where they rolled into its belly. From here the Earl launched them out again in furious fusillades of belching smoke and they fell on the fields beyond. Occasionally this bombardment would take out a cow – at which point the valiant nobleman would dance a jig of delight on the grass, pulling the powder monkey along in his train. Then he would halt and cuff the boy by the ears – the signal for him to return to his task – and shortly the onslaught would begin again.

The image of the third Earl, said by some to have been briefly an associate of Oswald Mosley in the early thirties, is another which is noticeably absent from the walls of the Hall.

A portrait was discovered by Mr Haines in a different corner of the attic to that of the Marquess. After staring at it for some time, he banished it to one of the outbuildings.

The writer is right to wonder why Mr Haines took him on for this job. Mr Haines is a careful man. He never takes an important decision without a great deal of thought. He does his research.

So the writer has 'done' the Baader-Meinhof gang, has he? And what exactly does that entail? Did he place himself inside the skin of Gudrun Ensslin? Did he pass his hands across the skeletal ribcage of Holger Meins? Did he look out through dark glasses from the skull of Andreas Baader? Did he do what Mr Haines has done?

'Satan Wants Me' – yes, Mr Haines has written a song by that name, based on the book, but it is a song written for a feature film. And the writer claims to be *researching* all this. After the success of the film *Christie Malry's Own Double Entry*, for which Mr Haines composed the soundtrack, the makers tried to come up with a film of *Satan Wants Me* and Mr Haines was commissioned to write the title song. Sadly the pitiful excuse for a British film industry has yet to come up with enough readies for the project to be given the green light. The writer would be well advised to read Mr Irwin's book, though. He might pick up some ideas on how to conceal secrets within a narrative.

It is unfortunate that the writer has failed to watch his copy of *Seance on a Wet Afternoon* – it might have added a little resonance to his experiences at the end of his time at the Hall. No matter – our own enjoyment of this period, when the time comes, will not be affected.

Excuse me a minute:

There's so much prattling amongst all this about the writer – it's supposed to be about Haines. WE'RE NOT INTERESTED IN YOU. Unfortunately, I'm going to have leave it in. Not just because of my ethics but because without it this slim volume would be even slimmer. We're going to have to think about changing the balance of this whole book, though. More me and less him.

The fact that Mr Haines himself does not appear in this chapter is an unfortunate necessity – what with him being engaged on other business at the time – but in his absence he is still a more potent force than the writer. And Mr Haines will – be assured of it – become ever stronger in the pages that follow.

Stevenson is a card, isn't he? He assures the writer that he will be comfortable in his quarters. Billy, the child abductor in *Seance* makes a similar promise to the girl he has 'borrowed'. I tend to put Stevenson's apparent ability to materialise and dematerialise at will down to the writer's lack of awareness of what is going on around him, more than to any magical powers on this gentleman's part, but I suppose you never know. Surely, though, the writer misses the point. The central issue here concerns Mr Haines and his own ability to flit through history in a variety of guises in order to make complex points about the webs of power and influence that control our lives today. Saint Germain figures in Mr Haines's song 'The Spook Manifesto'. Of which more later.

Well, anyway. On with the 'story'.

Day Two

I woke up with a ghostly screeching in my head. I opened my eyes – and then I sat bolt upright because it happened again. It was light in my room. I turned round. The curtain over my window was glowing. I looked at my watch – it was eight o'clock. I turned round again and peered through the curtains just as another terrible wail passed through the window into the room. It was a peacock. Sitting in the middle of the lawn.

The next thing I knew there was a knock on the door. It was the maid. She had a tray with tea on it. She put it on the table beside the bed.

'Breakfast is served in twenty minutes, sir,' she said, with another curtsy.

'What's your name, love?' I asked again. 'How long have you worked here?'

'It's not for me to linger in young gentlemen's bedrooms, sir, if you'll excuse me,' she said, and walked straight out again.

The tea was the same stuff as before. It was OK – I must be getting used to it.

Down in the dining hall, sunlight was pouring through the twenty-foot windows and bouncing down off the ceiling. Outside all you could see was acres of green and blue. My place was set where it had been the night before. More sunlight – projected in a golden grid on to the wood of the table.

Just inside the door there was a long table with a white cloth hanging over the sides in loops, piled with food. There were cereals, juices, racks of toast, croissants, marmalades, jams, tea and coffee. I filled a tray and took it to my place.

I unloaded the tray and arranged everything neatly – cereal bowl in front, toast to the left, tea to the right – just like I do back home. I'd just started eating when I heard a burst of laughter crack across from the far end of the hall. Through another doorway down there, two men, one in early middle age, the other in his twenties, and a young woman came in. A table had been laid with three places. They sat down and began chatting quietly. I couldn't catch much of what they were saying, but they had American accents. The woman looked familiar. She stared up at the older man when he spoke, but he only had eyes for the younger one. Then Stevenson came in through my door, carrying a tray with two silver salvers. He held it up to his chest but away from his body. He ignored me and headed off towards the Americans.

On his way back up, he crossed with the maid – she was on the way down there now with a coffee pot and some tea.

The new guests were tucking in, cramming in the food and talking at the same time. Bulging cheeks and mangled vowels. The younger man obviously wasn't satisfied with the food he had been brought, though. He got up and walked up the hall to the table where all the rest was. He started piling up a plate. I got up, too, and went over to grab some more toast.

'All right,' I said to him. He looked at me, nodded sharply and started walking back towards his table.

As soon as I finished eating, Stevenson was there, just behind me.

'Mr Haines wondered, sir,' he said, 'whether you would like to take a walk, to acquaint yourself with some of the grounds?'

'Yeah. Excellent,' I said. 'Cheers.' I pushed back my chair.

We made our way out towards the North Hall – but turned right instead of left.

There's another entrance hall there, leading to the south side of the building. The North Hall is grand, but this is better – it's got a quieter but richer beauty. It's the shape of an oval, and the colour of cream. Set into walls lined with pink marble columns, twenty-foot high, are niches so tall that giants could stand up in there. Ready to drop down, dip their heads and march out into the giant-sized gardens. The roof is like the inside of a massive meringue. At the top there's a glass window, another oval, latticed like a spider's web.

Stevenson opened the tall double doors and I walked through on to the terrace.

Peace. Serenity. Beauty. I never knew the real meaning of any of those words until I stood there, looking out over that view with Stevenson.

The flat stone canopy roof, held up by pillars, made it cool, but out there beyond it you could almost feel the heat of the day starting to build up in all that sky. The grass is dark green like the sea and as wide and deep. It stretches and stretches, drawing your eyes out of your head, down the slope to the swans gliding across the lake.

Stevenson sees it every day, but even he was just standing there, looking at it without saying a word.

Then he turned to me and said:

'If you wouldn't mind keeping within the confines of what you can see immediately in front of you, sir. Mr Haines would rather you didn't go past the lake or the line of trees on either side. Similarly, although the path at the bottom of the steps here continues to both your left and your right along the whole length of the house – and indeed much further – he would be obliged if you would not venture beyond the limits of the lawn. Feel free to stay out here as long as you like, sir, but morning coffee will be available in the silver urn in the dining hall from eleven.'

Down I went. There was more stone on either side of the steps, diagonal balustrades slicing through the air towards the grass. The stone was rough where the sun had toasted and blistered it over hundreds of years. Down at the bottom I stood on the pebbled path and looked along it to either side. It certainly did go a long way. To the right, it dipped down alongside a set of stone outbuildings, to the left it disappeared into trees.

I stretched my arms. Then I dropped them to my sides and

started walking. The grass was flat and even. No bare patches. No cigarette packets, beer cans or used condoms. No dogshit.

I went straight down the middle. The grass sloped downwards, which made it seem as though the trees on either side were getting taller. Beeches and pines and silver birch – with the only sound the wind in their leaves. I was heading for the lake. I wanted the water. And the swans. Beautiful white curved birds.

With the sound of tiny waves lapping underneath me, I stopped. I was on the edge of the lake. I barely saw the rushes and reeds. The water was a deeper, darker green than the grass, and filled with the reflections of sky and trees. I stared deep inside it, at the greyness of its white clouds.

The swans had moved away. They were over the other side now, preening. There were moorhens, too, and a couple of male mallard to the right with a female further over.

And then I turned round and looked back at the house. And sucked in my breath.

Walking away from it, I had given no thought to how it would look when I turned to face it for the first time. Now, suddenly, I saw the south face of the Hall laid out in front of me. The layers, the sections, the rows of windows and the lines of the pillars. Every column and balustrade and parapet, spanning the horizon from left to right, set back on that carpet of green, which flowed up now, like the train of a royal gown, drawing the eye up to an aristocratic peak. I could see the balance of the thing, the symmetry, the patterns, and the precision of the lines and angles. I could see the white and yellow and grey of the stone, the green slopes of the copper on the roof. Yesterday I'd watched as the front of the house gradually inched its way out to me, like a tanker turning, as I approached it. But this was full glory, full-on, first time. A gigantic wall of stone – no colonnades this side – raised in the middle by those pillars, given a triangle for a roof and raised again on the wings by arches. It's like a stone B52. Eighteenth-century shock and awe.

I turned back to the lake. What I wanted was to ignore what Stevenson had said. I wanted to disappear through those trees down there or cruise on past the water, through the woods towards that arch. But they might be watching me. Someone – Stevenson, probably – might be up there, behind me, at a high window, binoculars to his eyes. I'd do it later, I'd come out when it was dark and roam around.

Instead I walked the boundaries of the territory I had been given. To the west of the house there was nothing but dense trees. Passing along its main body, I stared at stone columns and arches, through huge windows into empty rooms and up at roof terraces and parapets. In the trees to the east I caught glimpses of the church and of gravestones in an overgrown churchyard. Finally I marched back up the grass, the Hall magnified further and further with every step until it blotted out the sky. Then I began once more to climb the steps, and a new, smaller, picture of that sky began to develop, and then I saw trees and then fields – the doors of both entrance halls were open. I could see clean through the building, from south to north.

Back in the dining room, I had coffee on my own. There were no Americans to ignore me this time. I wondered who they were. Maybe Haines is showing off his pile to rich foreigners for a stiff price? Selling a sight of England's heritage.

Back up to my room – typing this up. Then I notice, underneath the window, almost hidden by the curtain, a phone socket. Maybe I can get on the internet in here? I've already tried the wireless connection on the laptop – 'no networks available'. I can't even get the mobile to work down here – there's no signal. It's no big deal. There's no one to call.

I was still at the laptop when, at exactly one o'clock – the display in the corner of the screen had just ticked round – a bell started ringing down below. An old hand bell, a 'bring out your dead' bell. I made my way downstairs. I could feel the curled tail of the last of the reverberations lashing round the brickwork as I followed the curved handrail down towards ground level.

Down at the far end of the dining hall, the Americans were back. I half-listened to them again as I ate the mozzarella salad Stevenson had brought, and let my eyes wander around the hall. Occasional words escaped from their little speech bubbles, when they raised their voices, and shot down to my end of the room. 'Catherine'. 'Champagne'. 'Tonight'. Strangely, though, they didn't sound American any more. I watched them for a while. The balance of power within their little group seemed to have changed, too. The older man was flirting with the woman now. And she was all over the younger guy. Maybe they were some weird friends of Haines's? There's still no sign of him, by the way.

As soon as I'd finished, Stevenson was there next to me. As he picked up the plate, I said:

'I've noticed there's a phone line in my room. Is there any chance of getting an internet connection set up there?'

'Ah,' he said – almost as if he'd been waiting for me to ask. 'I'm sure that could be arranged, sir. If you would like to leave your machine with me along with all the necessary information, I'm sure we could have something up and running for you by the time you return.'

'Return?'

'Yes, sir, I have taken the liberty of arranging a little sightseeing trip for you this afternoon. If you could be in the North Hall at two thirty, sir, then we can proceed from there.'

'Cheers, Stevenson. I'll be there.'

Stevenson was wearing a tweed cap and a green jacket and he was sitting in an old Land Rover.

He was smiling as we moved off, but not at me, he was staring in front of him. We turned right past the statues of Paradis and Valentino and headed east through the barbed-wire covered arch at the end of the colonnade. It looks new, that wire – there's no sign of any rust. The car was kicking up plenty of dust as we followed the road round to the right – and then we were moving parallel to a river, the car bucking with the bumps in the road, the water smooth and slow and full of tiny, icy reflections. Ahead on the left I could see the blurred shape of some kind of giant metal sculpture. It looked as though it was on fire – there was smoke billowing out from either side of it.

Stevenson pulled up twenty yards short of it and we got out. It was a model of a Cessna aircraft, clamped to a massive metal bracket. Straddling the fuselage was a goggled, helmeted mannequin – a wingwalker in crinolines with a mouthpiece in front of her. There's a song of Haines's called 'Light Aircraft on Fire' – I think it's about mental disintegration. This is some kind of portrayal of it.

As we got closer we could see into the cabin. It was lit with orange and red light. The mannequin pilot, in World War Two flying gear, was hunched over the controls, frozen in the act of screaming into a radio mike. At his back there was a devilish figure in black, teeth bared. Stevenson was staring at the plane with his hands in his pockets.

'Bridging the gap between thought and expression sometimes brings such pain,' he murmured.

The burning plane by the river, the fields behind it, the sky above. In the background a classical stone bridge.

'Shall we move on, sir?' he asked.

He was already walking towards the car.

'Don't forget your seatbelt, will you, sir?' said Stevenson. 'We wouldn't want any misfortune to befall you while you are in our company.'

We were off again and heading for the bridge – it was side-on in front of us. Its central section, bordered with stone pillars, is like a tiny temple. At either end there are symmetrical arches. I could see a female figure in white stone, lying across the ramparts. As we straightened up towards it, I could see another reclining woman on the other side. Crossing the shiny, dark river, I looked out to my right to see an alabaster Patty Hearst, and then we were in the shade of the stone roof for a second, trees flitting past through the columns, and then we were out the other end and passing two more female nudes spread out on either side before we hit the open road again.

'I noticed Patty Hearst,' I said to Stevenson, lifting my voice above the noise of the engine, 'but who are the others?'

'Miss Unity Mitford, sir,' he replied without turning his head, 'and, on this side, Miss Leila Khaled and Miss Gudrun Ensslin.'

To our left there was an open field of rough grass, beyond it a wooden fence and behind that a thick wood. The river on our right had disappeared. Instead there were two overgrown tennis courts, behind wire fences. The nets were still up, but they were sagging and holed and there were weeds and thistles growing out of the ground, some knee-high. To the left of the tennis courts, and following the road, the grass opened up again and sloped upwards past a huge silver birch. In the distance we could see a building like a small, thin castle, made out of red stone.

Halfway towards this building, the road narrowed. There was a sort of lay-by, or maybe a passing place, on the left and Stevenson pulled into it. Ahead, just off the road and at an angle to it, was a green sports car with the driver's door open. There was a body lying on the verge next to it. Stevenson and I got out of the car and walked towards it. Stevenson walked slowly, his expression calm.

Underneath the car was a pool of black oil in a perfect circle. I saw now that actually the body was a blonde mannequin, dressed in an expensive suit. Her legs were delicately bent and her arms read eight o'clock. There was blood coming out of her mouth in a streak across her cheek. It perfectly matched her lipstick. Her stare looked too blank for the victim of a traffic accident. Stevenson was tutting and walking forwards – her skirt had ridden up. He pulled it down over her knees. Then he took a perfectly folded white handkerchief from his pocket and flicked it across her hair to remove some leaves, before using it to wipe some birdshit from her face.

'Remind me to return later with my hairbrush and cloth, would you please, sir?' he asked. And then he added: 'At least the foxes haven't been back.'

After the Auteurs, Haines had a band called Black Box Recorder. Their first song was called 'Girl Singing in the Wreckage'. It's about a young woman looking back over her life from the scene of her death. Car crashes and plane crashes are specialities for Haines. They're symptomatic of dismembered lives and people getting wrecked. You get accidents and airports and terrorists and breakdowns in his songs. And bombs and murder and terrorists with children.

We were on our way back to the car again. The sky was turning a smoky grey, and dark clouds were building behind the castle.

As we passed the silver birch, its trunk, set against the deep purple of the clouds, shone brightly in a sudden burst of sunlight like a giant streak of lightning.

The road took us close to the red castle. It has three towers – one on the right that looks like Big Ben and two next to each other on the left with domes at the top. In between there's a deeper section, pushed back as if it's being concealed, with another of those triangular roofs. There are two doors there and three windows above and then another, tiny window, maybe leading to an attic, above that – it looks like the kind of place where the mad woman always lives in films. In front of the doors there were two giant helium-filled balloon figures – a pair of fat boys dressed in Victorian school uniforms, caps perched on top of round heads. They were bobbing in the breeze, as if trying to escape their wires.

'Who are they?' I asked Stevenson.

Stevenson frowned.

'Those, sir, are the Deverell Twins.'

Yes. 'The Deverell Twins' is another Black Box Recorder song. They entice a young girl to her death in the River Thames. She's a willing victim – in love with herself and with the thought of dying. A modern girl, but drawn to the bridge where the Deverells jumped and drowned a hundred years earlier. Drawn to the water. Like Jessica. But Jessica didn't want to die. Jessica wasn't in love with herself. Jessica... Anyway, somehow they grab this girl across the years – it's a psychogeographical killing. Is that why they're moving in the wind here – are they trying to escape from the place where they've been trapped, so they can find another victim?

We didn't stop outside the castle. We passed it on our right and then we met the river again and carried on alongside it like before. I stared into it, it was shallower here, but fast-moving – thick cords of current above its bed, like the twisted branches of old trees. On its far side, squatting in the bushes, was a circular stone building with a domed roof and a ring of columns outside a central hub with a dark doorway – like some eighteenth-century spaceship.

We stopped again and got out of the car. Set back from the road, there was a curved wall, about six feet high and thirty feet long. At regular intervals there were alcoves with busts in them. In the middle was a stone slab and above that a pyramid with an egg-shaped hollow.

Stevenson stood where he was as I walked along the line of heads and half-chests. Their skin is pitted with white crust – and other parts are going green. They don't have eyes, just featureless blobs. They look like aliens.

In the oval recess of the pyramid, there was an eggcup with a tiny Humpty Dumpty inside. Stevenson had appeared beside me.

'We are Grade One listed, sir,' he said. 'Mr Haines is unable to remove, deface or in any way damage any of the buildings, statues or monuments in the grounds, and this applies also, of course, to the Hall itself. He is happy to be able to add, adorn, comment and contradict while respecting our English Heritage. Only by preserving the past do we really know how far we have come, is that not so, sir?'

Back in the car, the road curved again. Soon we were nearly back where we started – close to the barbed-wire arch – and we passed a statue that we'd seen on our right on the way out. It's set on a plinth halfway between the arch and the wood concealing the tiny church, and it's an image from the sleeve of an Auteurs album, *Now I'm a Cowboy*. It's a statue of a young boy in a lamé jacket, but you can't tell whether it's gold or silver. The cover was in black and white and the statue is the same. His hands are folded in front of him. The jacket is a mixture of dark and light. Passing it this time, I had a better view of the statue – the kid has a black eye and a mask of freckles and his jacket isn't straight. His white shirt is buttoned up but he doesn't have a tie. His head's tilted and he's frowning slightly. On the first Auteurs album, *New Wave*, there's a song called 'Starstruck'. It's about a vaudeville actor who was put on the stage when he was five. That's how old

Haines was when his neighbour's young son disappeared. He wrote a song about it – 'Unsolved Child Murder'. Innocence seems to vanish after five for him. I know what he means. If I could freeze myself at any age, I'd choose the moment just before that happens. When you still believe that the world is a place to play in – and you're living it to the full. I want to remember what it was like to be that age. That's nothing to do with nostalgia, though. It's about reclaiming passion and intensity and clarity of vision. If you genuinely lose a part of you, as opposed to shedding something you've outgrown, you should go back and look for it. Yeah, I'd freeze myself at five. Just before Jessica died. She was my sister. She drowned in a lake. They jumped in and pulled her out, but it was too late.

Lunch was homemade vegetable lasagne, baked potato with a choice of five grated cheeses, tomato and onion salad, fresh orange juice. Apple pie and custard. Turns out the chef – who's called Henri – once worked in a vegetarian restaurant.

Stevenson has given up with the 'Mr Haines regrets' stuff now. He didn't even mention him. Although I've got the laptop back, I can't get on to the internet. The connection looks fine but I can't access any sites or download any email. Some kind of technical problem according to Stevenson. He says they're working on it.

After lunch I was invited to the drawing room. Stevenson showed me the way, but he needn't have bothered – straight back along the main corridor, through the entrance hall, first left. He obviously doesn't want me wandering off.

Standing in the drawing room is like being inside a giant, gold-panelled box. Different shades of metallic yellow decorate the walls – rectangles inside rectangles, squares inside squares. Shiny right-angled gilt with gilded snaking patterns. You can imagine the lords and ladies in here, when this place was at its peak, gathered in front of a grand piano in neat rows – lines of motionless powdered white wigs. But all that's in there now is a row of three chairs – facing another one on its own. That was my chair. Stevenson pointed me towards it and then he was gone, the door closing silently behind him.

Then the door opened again and in came the two men and

the woman from the dining hall. They walked straight past me towards the row of chairs. The woman and the older man moved behind them and the other man sat on the one in the middle, putting a suitcase on the floor next to him. They all looked straight at me for what could have been a count of ten. I recognised the woman now. It was Haines's wife, Catherine. There'd been photos in the papers and magazines.

Catherine and the two men began to act out a scenario. They were a family – the older man and Catherine the parents, and the younger man their son. The parents were arguing about money drying up and bills mounting. The son was staring into space above my head.

Suddenly the father snapped at him.

'You're showing us up,' he said, looking down on him. 'We've got our pride, you know. Even if it's all we got. People look at you in your rags and say, "See how they look after him." Show some respect. Get yourself a decent suit – we pay you, don't we? Maybe it'll give you a bit of self-respect, too.'

The 'boy' just sat there. Then the parents began talking about 'the act' – they were part of a circus that had fallen on hard times. They went on about the old days and how nobody wanted their kind of stuff any more. 'Forty years,' said the father. 'And they throw us into the wilderness.' He reached into his pocket and produced three coloured balls. He moved out from behind the chairs and began to juggle with them, hurling them high into the air and watching them arc and fall. Then Catherine moved out to join him. He changed the trajectory of the balls. One by one they landed in Catherine's outstretched hands and she put them in her jacket pocket. He bowed, she curtsied, and then they walked over to the window where they stood, looking out and whispering to each other. The 'boy' reached into the suitcase and took out an overcoat and a trilby. He stood up and put them on.

'I was part of the act as soon as I could walk,' he said. 'Grew up with it, grew into it. And then grew out of it. I wanted more, wanted to go out on my own. So I left them. Left my family, left the act. Forsook them, Dad said. Can you imagine what it took to do that? Knowing what would happen? Because they didn't survive it, you see. That was the end for them, the end of the act. Decades of family history. But I had to go. Because it was written in the stars. That I was going to become a star. All I had to do was leave, strike out on my own, and it would just happen. That's what I thought. But there is no destiny, there is no fate. You make your own luck. And the truth is I wasn't good enough. Not good enough to make my own luck.'

He loosened his tie. He reached down into the suitcase, grabbed a whisky bottle and took a swig.

'But I did meet Tara. I wouldn't say she had made it but at least she was working regular. We fell in love. It didn't matter to either of us that I had no money because we both knew I was going to make it any minute. Any moment, we kept saying, it's going to happen. The phone's going to ring – my big break. I was so sure of it I even convinced her, you see. And then, later, when I began to lose hope, it was her turn to convince me. We were married by then. But nothing was happening. The stardust wasn't falling. We were living off what she brought in. So one day she cut her losses. She left me. For my agent. My agent. Joe Stantini. You know him? You heard of him?' He leaned towards me. 'No? You're lucky. "Just another couple of hundred for expenses, Sam," he'd say. "This time next month you'll be a star." Weasel.'

He took another slug on the whisky bottle.

'And then I met Rick.'

The other actor returned from the window and stood next to him. He, too, reached into the suitcase, and took out a trilby. Then he pulled up the collars of his jacket and stuck his hands into his pockets.

'I got a proper job,' said Sam. 'If you can call it that. Valeting cars. Rick was a doorman. And a thief. We got on pretty well. He was dumb but he did what I said.'

Rick laughed.

'One night we broke into Stantini's. Trashed the place.'

Rick was nodding and punching one fist into the other. Sam's face had lit up into a huge, lopsided grin.

'We stole everything he had! Everything he couldn't live without, everything that meant anything to him – papers,

money, black book, notebooks, the framed photos on his desk.
The rest of it we trashed. Best night of my life.'

Rick had moved back now. He was standing a few feet
behind, side-on, lighting a cigarette.

Sam's manic smile eased. He put down the whisky bottle.

Catherine had moved out from her position by the window.
She came and sat down next to him. She crossed her legs and
he took her hand.

'But that's all in the past. 'Cos I met Rita, see? And we're
happy. Rita used to be a showgirl. I used to be a second-rate
actor. It's a perfect fit. But no one knows what we were. Only
what we are. And that's happy together.'

They looked into each other's eyes and smiled.

Then they stood, Rick joined them, and they picked up the
chairs and lined them neatly against the wall. Sam took Rick's
trilby and packed the suitcase. Rick folded down his collars.
Sam took a look around and then glanced at the other two.
They nodded at him. He turned and led them off, the whisky
still in his hand. As they reached the door he paused to knock
back another mouthful – and then they were gone.

The skit had been based on the songs on *New Wave*. Songs
of disenchantment, envy and escape. I wandered over to the
window and looked out. I looked down the road I had walked
along to get here – as far as the bend which took it out of
sight. What would happen if I just packed my things, set off
down the corridor, out of the front door and began heading
back down that road? Would they come after me? And if so,
who? Stevenson? Or Haines – would he come rushing out from
wherever he's hiding and announce his existence? He could be
anywhere in this place. He could hide here for weeks and I'd
never know. But why invite me here and then disappear?

I went back outside. I looked down the corridor and wondered
whether to chance a bit of exploration. More dark wood down
there and dark doors, a red carpet, something that looked like
it might be a coat of arms hanging on a wall, another staircase.
But maybe it would be best to start outside – less chance of
being seen. And to wait till night.

Stevenson had a chat with me over supper (cheese bake and

vegetable risotto – another gem from Henri). He was standing at my shoulder again. I tried to get him to sit down but of course he wouldn't. He stood with his hands behind his back and began to tell me some of the history of the place. A bunch of aristocrats owned it before the American guy – passing it down, father to son. Stevenson started by pointing out the ceiling:

'The plaster is George IV, sir. Note the exquisite carvings of fish, fruit and game around the edges.'

On either side of the pillars, where they meet the ceiling, there are niches with carved figures inside. Stevenson told me that they were 'The First Earl's Beasts'.

'You will notice, sir, how the Gothic ribs of the pillars support both the finery of the ceiling and the Beasts themselves – and that each Beast in turn supports a vane,' he said.

Oswald Mosley stayed here a couple of times in the early thirties, according to Stevenson. Sounding out the third Earl, apparently. There were German visitors, too, then – arriving by night and leaving in the small hours. Whatever happened at these meetings – and Stevenson either didn't know or wasn't telling – by the time war broke out, the Earl was reckoned to be resolutely on side. King and country and a desk job in the War Office.

I've just finished typing all this up. I wanted to explore but I'm falling asleep. There are strange sounds outside again, but it can't be peacocks this time of night. And anyway it sounds deeper, human – or inhuman. More than one voice but much further off.

Tomorrow night I'm going out there. I want to find out what's going on.

Editor's note—

First, some random thoughts:

The writer seems to be getting a bit edgy – already.

Vegetarians should not be allowed to be writers. The lack of animal blood in their diet atrophies the neurones connecting present-day civilised man to the spear-carrying ghost in the back of the brain, thus removing the holistic objectivity so vital to the practising of the literary art. Or something.

Yes, Mr Haines is an omnivore. He eats both white bread and red meat.

Right. All the stuff about the pretty surroundings is self-indulgent, indolent crap. It's just there – live with it. I suppose, though, it's 'scene-setting' at some basic level... Hm. OK, we'll leave it in. I certainly can't be arsed doing it myself.

The writer seems to be imagining that he is somehow sharing a moment with Stevenson, looking out across the southern aspect. Sharing a moment with Stevenson? Truly sharing anything with Stevenson? Does he not realise how difficult that would be? If he only knew what that man has seen in his lifetime. Pumping away with that four-pounder from the roof of the Hotel Majestic in Beirut. Speeding away, lights off, in Belfast from the pursuing IRA car with its tail-seeking missile. Selling those 'unwanted' Army rifles. They were unwanted, weren't they? If the Army had wanted them they would have looked after them a little better, would they not? There is only so much of that life that you can take. Only for so long can you resist your true vocation. Only for so long can you fail to answer the call of your elderly father to come home – the father who had been forced to wait until the advanced age of fifty-two before being able finally to celebrate the prized birth of a male child. Time it was, then, when the growing weakness of that call made the necessity of responding to it ever stronger, to return and to begin again. At the beginning. And to aim, far-off, for the end. Time to become a butler.

The writer wants to travel to parts of the estate that are forbidden to him. One place he yearns to visit is the Viscount's Arch. He will never do so. I suspect that, due to the Arch's distance from the Hall, he has pencilled in the visit for a later date during his stay. By the time he reaches that date, though, he will long since have given up exploring. This is a shame as it would have been interesting to see how such a visit turned out. The Viscount's Arch is the one spot on Mr Haines's territory from which it might be possible, given good luck and a following wind, to make an athletic bid for freedom. Ah well, some things are not meant to be.

Interesting, the fear of being watched. Early signs of paranoia. Chill out. Don't take it all so seriously. Not yet. Anyway, it's only a game. That is what Billy, the kidnapper, tells the girl in *Seance on a Wet Afternoon*. It is what he tells himself, too. That he is playing a 'joke'. That he is merely 'borrowing' a child. On his way to collect the ransom he stands in front of a cinema poster for *Billy Liar*. It is his wife, the deeply disturbed Myra, who has written in her kidnap note that they are 'professionals' and that they 'mean business'. It is she who threatens the parents of the child that they will never see their daughter alive again. She accuses Billy of a lack of imagination, of not being able to stretch far enough to reach the truth.

It is unlikely to be Stevenson behind those net curtains. He is such a busy man. It is the landed gentry who have all the time in the world. That is what makes them so dangerous. "Never work" is their motto. Toil is so draining, they say. Leave it to the lower classes. We must be free to concentrate on other things.

Mr Haines 'selling a sight of England's heritage'? No, his business takes other forms. Out of the writer's sight, he is creating another vision – out in the undergrowth and behind the trees. A vision of past, present and future.

Would you surrender your computer, passwords and all, to someone you did not trust?

The arch through which Stevenson drives the writer is Doric. This thought leads me to recall a story by HP Lovecraft. It is called 'The Case of Charles Dexter Ward'. Ward lives in a Georgian mansion with Doric arches. He is '… blond, with studious eyes and a slight droop, dressed somewhat carelessly…' Sounds a bit like Mr Haines. Dexter Ward was an early practitioner of what Guy Debord would later christen the 'dérive', a psychogeographical 'drifting' he developed from André Breton's wanderings across Paris in search of real life. Where is my Lovecraft? Ah here it is. I quote. Ward's:

'… walks were always adventures in antiquity, during which

he managed to recapture from the myriad relics of a glamorous old city a vivid and connected picture of the centuries before.'

The light aircraft – yes, a Cessna 350. To see it only as a fixed image, though, to fail to appreciate its mise-en-scène, to fail to perceive its life and its perpetual, eternal tipping into death – innocence or stupidity?

The writer comments that the attic in the 'castle' – he means the Temple of Pity – would serve well as a haunt for the traditional Gothic madwoman. This is interesting because there was such a lady in residence during the time of the first Earl. In fact it was his wife. She became hysterical after her husband, having succeeded in impregnating her with the second Earl, refused ever to indulge in sexual congress with her again. The poor woman was eventually moved to this temple where, it was said, her hysteria could be ministered to by her doctor in the kind of calm and tranquil setting best able to bring about her recovery. Here her cries travelled across the bare slopes and sank into the infertile soil. By the time rumours spread about her terrible confinement, and words were finally spoken to the Earl (who seemed to have forgotten she existed) by his advisers, she had become truly deranged. She spent the rest of her sad life in that attic, recognised sorrowfully by society as a true lunatic. Here she quaffed laudanum and disappeared into a world which, it is to be hoped, was more pleasurable than the one which she left.

Yes, one needs to be strong to live in an attic. Like Stevenson. There is no chance of sexual hysteria there.

Ah, we hear of the writer's sister. And of her tragic watery demise. 'Jessica...' The ellipsis is mine. The writer left the name hanging there without any punctuation, but he did not cross it out. There was a definite sense of something missing. I wonder if she speaks to him as Myra's stillborn son, Arthur, speaks to her. If so, I do hope she is a sight more pleasant!

'The Deverell Twins'. Yes, but what is the song asking? That the innocent somehow will the abuse they receive from the experienced, perhaps? There is an earlier song by Mr Haines entitled 'Child Brides'. Two young girls, each newly married, are drawn into the waves by Neptune. The girls' male relatives come looking for them. But they are not there. They are under the waves with the god of the sea.

I like Stevenson's little line about the foxes, although it was obviously lost on the writer. What would foxes want with a lump of plastic?

The writer misses both the freemasonic significance of the pyramid and the identities of Messrs Fludd, Digby, Norgate etc. Aliens indeed, in this modern world. Not to worry, though. It is not important.

The writer discusses the significance of the age of five for Mr Haines. Significant, too, is the age of minus five. It was in 1962, five years before the great man's birth that Bryan Forbes began writing *Seance on a Wet Afternoon*.

Ah – Catherine. Now there's a woman. And so we hear a little more of the tale that has been spun about her and Mr Haines. We are told that these persons met in Las Vegas. Where she, once middle class, newly rich, was apparently already slumming it – in search of the flip-side of life, looking for flies. Nightclubbing and go-go dancing. A showgirl – and lap dancer, too, we hear. But surely this is too rich – are we seriously to believe it all? Are we to breathe in the pungent aroma from this imbalanced pot-pourri of elements from Mr Haines's *New Wave* album and to pronounce that it smells sweet? I feel my credence failing. Are we, in fact, to believe any of this? It all seems – to we who know something now of the real Mr Haines – so unlikely. But the writer is so eager to accept what he reads. So trusting. Apparently this quality is sometimes looked on as a virtue. Well then, let us briefly take on board what he has accepted and travel with him a short way on this now rather bizarre journey. The accounts have it that this 'Haines' was the archetypal bored Englishman looking for 'a bit of skirt', and that he chatted up this young lady. Not that she was wearing such an item of apparel, we hear – or much else. But, come on, has our Mr Haines ever been the archetypal anything? I mean, some of this reads like the kind of rubbish you make up for the tabloids! Well, anyway, let us go with it a while longer. One thing led to another, we are told. The 'young lady', however, did not tell her 'beau' who she really was. Not until he had asked her to marry him. Sensible girl, the observers agree. But perhaps at this point we should extend our indulgence and be positively charitable! Yes, let us momentarily please these commentators, and the writer – and perhaps even, if we may temporarily suspend our fundamental disbelief, ourselves! – and, for that short time, get into the spirit of this tale. Yes, let us pause and imagine briefly how this 'happy couple' would have enjoyed being out on the West Coast for a both-in-white 'LA wedding'! The sun (Mr Haines keeping his hat on), the people (Mr Haines and his walking stick with the metal tip), the lack of public transport cluttering up the roads! And what a wonderful chance, too, for the great man to view the enemy at close quarters – and to see whether England looked different from the other side of the pond. Ah, what a marvellous vision we have created for our hero! Oh, and for his lovely 'bride', too, of course – I apologise for forgetting her there in my excitement. Dear 'Catherine'. But sadly there would be no opportunity in our story to dally in the city of angels, even at such a time as this – for there would, of course, be a new life beckoning back at home. And so, inevitably, the fairy tale ends with a return to England and the taking up by the new 'husband and wife' of joint residence at the Hall. How neat! How sweet! How unlike the lives that the rest of us live! What is undeniably true, however, in this nefariously nebulous narrative is that Mr Haines has now ensconced himself within his new country home. And taken charge there. Yes, he has become 'Lord Luke'. To all intents and purposes.

New Wave. Mr Haines as Rudolph Valentino on the front cover. Life on this record is experienced as failure – after which, it says, one must force oneself to one's feet, grab self-respect in the face of adversity and make one's own luck. Lessons to us all here, I think. The record features dancing girls, wingwalkers and showgirls. And actors. It deals with stars and starlight and the star system. And answers the question 'Is it all in the stars?' with a resounding no. But let us not forget that it also deals with revenge. And criminals. Working together. And betraying each other. If they can do that to their pals, imagine what they do to the nice guys.

A digression. I happen to know that one of the (presumably unopened) books in the writer's room was Michael Bracewell's *England is Mine*. Bracewell's book is a cultural history of literate English rock music. But it does not mention Mr Haines. Black Box Recorder's *England Made Me* album came out soon after this tome appeared. 'Always get the last word' is one of Mr Haines's mottoes. This title comes, of course, from the novel by Graham Greene. Mr Haines is a big admirer of Greene. *Brighton Rock* was a big influence: kids and violence, English gangs, seedy towns. Very resonant. Very useful. Bracewell says that Greene's originality and wit came from his position between Arcady and suburbia – that suburbia was their spur. Mr Haines had both feet in suburbia, early on – but he was looking towards Arcady. Bracewell talks about the way the English suburbs pour out song writers who comment acerbically and profoundly on their environment. But – sorry to repeat this (actually, no, I'm not sorry) – he doesn't even mention Mr Haines. He says that alternative thinking in English culture in the twentieth century often combines visionary poetics and political subversion. And (yes, I am going to say it again) – *he doesn't even mention Mr Haines.*

Arcady was handed over to the suburbs in the twenties and thirties, says Bracewell. Well, the Hall is one part that was not. It was not until much later that Mr Haines left the suburbs and grabbed it for himself. The Arcadian vision is infantilist, says Bracewell. Not so Mr Haines's. And his own version of Arcadianism has been severely doctored and personalised.

Bracewell says that the first paradox of Arcady is its capture and imprisonment by the rich – the end of the rural democracy ruled over by nature. Well, perhaps letting the writer walk in the midst of it this morning was one small step towards redemocratising it. 'Arcadianism'. 'Pastoral simplicity', says my dictionary. Sums up the writer's gobsmacked attitude to all this, I suppose.

If the writer began to walk out of here would Mr Haines leave his hiding place and run after him? What kind of question is that? The question of a dolt!

The first Earl's Beasts. Mythical figures, apparently made

to the Earl's own designs. Lustful, priapic creatures, each with a penis reaching the ceiling but concealed from the view of those standing below by the backs of the Beasts' introverted bodies. But the Earl knew what was there, each time he raised his head to the roof, and that was the main thing. And the lords, ladies – and even kings – alongside him did not. Which tickled him enormously.

There was so much more to Stevenson's description of the Hall and its past but the writer seems to have failed to record it. What a waste of that fine man's time and energy. But no matter. We have found alternative ways of recounting it. Try not to let your eyes and brain glaze over, writer, when Stevenson gives you a history lesson. He is trying to help you link the past to the present. It is the only way to tell the future.

See how the writer's desire to explore dissipates at the sound of a few unusual noises! Stiffen your sinews and straighten your spine, man! There is worse ahead of you.

Now, as the writer has so far failed in his attempts to gain the ears of Mr Haines, I have felt it necessary to seek my own audience with the great man. We are desperately in need of some biographical information on him.

He has graciously responded to my request in the affirmative and has provided me with some background to the Hainesian life.

So here we are then. Here is Mr Haines. I am sure that we were all beginning to think that we would never meet him.

Mr Haines is a man whose music is essence of pop, spiced with misanthropy and fomented in radical fervour – then cooked up in a pressure cooker of political intrigue. A writer who is stock of Ray Davies, Rotten and Morrissey, garnished with extract of Dylan, Reed and Cohen – bottled and booted across the Atlantic. An Auteur, a politico-historical analyst, a wit and iconoclast – a Wilde, Whistler and Wyndham Lewis for the post-modern generation. And he is with us now!

I conversed with the subject of our tale as he was sitting in a carved armchair in his private apartment at the Hall, a table by his side on which was a bottle of whisky, a single glass and a revolver. His feet were resting on an ancient stool with a red velvet cover. He was wearing a red and white silk smoking jacket and black trousers with a single red stripe running down each leg.

I admired his chair. He informed me that the wood was cut from the elm tree that stood behind the English lines at the Battle of Waterloo. The cabinet in the corner of the room – he gave a regal wave in its direction – is apparently full of Napoleonic relics. A jewelled sword, an *escritoire d'or*. A silver-gilt dish and plate. All captured at Waterloo. Napoleon, he told me, begged to be allowed British citizenship after his defeat. We proceeded.

Mr Haines informed me that he was born in Walton on Thames, deep in the mythical South of England, on October 7th 1967, and is an only child. This, he says, helped him to 'forge a strong sense of independence.' He preferred his own company as a nipper but does not recall feeling lonely.

At this point a little Blake drifts back to me:

'… *from the Valleys of Walton and Esher… Jerusalem's pillars fall…*'

According to Mr Haines, an upbringing in Surrey brings a psychogeographical connection that is unique in our land:

'Vic Godard – the "last of the Surrey people" – knows all about it,' he said. 'And Jimmy Pursey. The Surrey people have an almost occult bonding with the place, more so than any other kin. We just don't feel the need to go on about it.'

Vic Godard – leader of Subway Sect, avant-punk innovators, latter-day crooner, man of Surrey. Jimmy Pursey, main man of punk shouters Sham 69. Haines, Godard and Pursey – a Surrey supergroup perhaps?

Ah, a little more Blake returns to me:

'*In all the dark Atlantic vale down from the hills of Surrey A black water accumulates: return, Albion! Return.*'

The twelve sons of Albion are named after Blake's enemies. Not even Mr Haines has taken literary revenge on that level.

On occasion, apparently, young Master Haines was dragged away from Walton to holiday in exotic places:

'We used to go to the Channel Islands,' he said, 'and stay in horrible Pontins type camps.' He shifted uneasily in his chair at the memory. 'They used to show films on a projector – weird obscure spaghetti westerns. *A Town Called Bastard* – that was definitely one. The Shads played there one year. One of the best shows I've ever seen.'

Yes, the Shadows. Hank Marvin. So much more authoritative a figure than, say, Jimmy Page. Page claimed Crowley – but Marvin had Cliff.

Mr Haines grew up in the glam-spangled seventies – a brightness in the shadow cast by the spectacle of the American sun. He soon began to develop an interest in music:

'Gary G. The Sweet, Suzi Q down in Devil Gate Drive. In my early teens I managed to hang out with the older kids, the ones who had by then left school, and were already liking Black Sabbath – and Alice Cooper ironically.'

Mr Cooper's cry of 'School's Out' was something that Mr Haines, too, wanted to hear. He was not suited to the regimentation and discipline of the classroom and playing field. He had his own, better ideas about what he should be learning. There was, though, always the charm of music to soothe his savage breast:

'There were a few kids who liked the same music,' he recalled to me, 'but their emphasis was on keeping it well punky – I'm talking 1980-1982. *Raw Power* was a good common ground and Pistols, Subway Sect and Buzzcocks were good. There would be a handful of kids in every provincial town walking around with 999 armbands on. Total amateurs. I lived for the Fall and the Velvets. I also loved Syd Barrett's Pink Floyd. I was seen as having eccentric yet superior tastes.'

Mr Haines went on to make an interesting comment:

'It's worth making the soon to be trite point,' he said, 'that in provincial England during the early 1980s, Velvet Underground records were a lot harder to get hold of than they are now. The internet has devalued music by enabling supply to outweigh demand.'

Indeed. What is the use, for example, of re-releasing Mr Haines's records? One can buy them second hand on eBay for half the price. (Obviously the original owners must have died. Or been incarcerated in homes for the insane). Original copies of these records are iconic. One should have to struggle to get hold of them. One should have to search long and hard, one should have to wait for long periods before one glimpses them – and ideally travel long distances in order to seize one. And, of course, Mr Haines cannot make any money this way. One wonders how this artist, this mainstay of British culture, would survive if he did not have his new-found wealth.

Well, he would 'work', of course. As he has always done. Not like the rest of them do, though, scrabbling around in the dirt. He would create. The same as he always did. Because talent will out. Ability will be rewarded. And an imagination will create new life. The line about a prophet never being acknowledged in his own land is surely true. And it is no less true now that Mr Haines is a man of property and material substance.

In fact, things are apparently even worse now for Mr Haines. Because his new-found status is all that interests anyone. Country house porn. Journalists and TV producers hassle him to reveal all. But I realise that I may just have inadvertently compared him to Christ. Let us have none of that.

Actually, Mr Haines has already written a whole song doing just that – sort of. Although he might argue that actually it is about false gods. And not actually hubris on a massive scale. The song concerns revolution, too – Mr Haines portrays himself as the revolutionary that Christ was prevented from being, the destroyer of the old order. For Mr Haines, though, the revolution will be characterised by his own kind of puritanism. He informed me that he would have been a Royalist in the Civil War:

'Definitely up for conscription, me, apart from Cromwell and wretched republicans. I will fight for this land but only alongside king or queen.'

I believe, however, that this view is espoused purely for public consumption. I believe that actually he would have been a grim and grey presence at Cromwell's right hand. Possibly Mr Haines's statement came as the result of his recent 'ennoblement'. If so, it was an understandable aberration.

Mr Haines's parents are, he says, 'God-fearing in a C of E kind of way. My mother's a retired school teacher. English and Religious Education.' Mr Haines's father, retired, too now, served as a graphic designer for the civil service – Royal Navy.

Struck by images of Blighty's strikes and terrorism, Mr Haines sat at home and lifted the corner of his mouth in a sneer at the thought that anyone would seriously want to work as much as a three-day week. He felt the tug of London, but also his suburban distance from it. He wanted to be there, inside it, but to keep his distance from it where it mattered – inside his head. At home he watched television: *Top of the Pops*, *The Persuaders* and old war films, and he read books: *Treasure Island*, *Billy Liar* and HP Lovecraft. And, of course, he seethed.

And, as soon as he could, Mr Haines made that journey – he went to London. In late August 1985 he left the delightful dormitory town of Portsmouth, where he had been 'studying' art. Art was dead. If he had wanted to prod and poke corpses he would have become a medical student. Mr Haines was heading for Brixton in South London – it was the weekend of the second riots. I myself remember being pursued in that locality that very weekend by a crew of skinheads and being forced to take refuge, head first, in the hedge of a front garden! Mr Haines was to take up residence there with what he describes as some 'eighties-style doleites'. Having received a scholarship, Mr Haines was shortly to begin 'studying' guitar, piano and composition at the London College of Music – in reality, of course, just another way to avoid work. A 'small reserve of optimism,' he informed me, 'had held out that music college would have the odd John Cale type smashing down on the piano keys. Instead it was just the usual fat tuba players from Huddersfield putting up posters about real ale etc.'

London was dull. Britain was dull. Punk had come and gone. The kids were dozing. The kids were shoe-gazing. Only

Mr Haines was looking around him. He despised most of what he saw but he paid attention and noted it, nevertheless – and then he shifted his gaze towards the Land of the Free. There was a little modern mythology over there that took his fancy. Not to mention plenty more to despise.

By this stage, Mr Haines had already perfected his 'Oxfam chic look.' Even in the early Auteurs photos, he says, he is 'wearing Oxfam clothes. Until I could afford something better.'

If only the haute couture designers whose windows he would skulk past during his perambulations in the West End had known who he was. He might have been able to give them a pre-emptive endorsement in exchange for a few of their tawdry rags.

Mr Haines had always known, he says, that he was going to be a good song writer. It just took him 'from age 15 to 24 to hone it.' Halfway through his college tenure he joined a pop group called the Servants, a moderately cheerful band of indie warblers and janglers. Even future stars need to start somewhere, and this was Mr Haines's rock and roll 'apprenticeship'. (Not many deserve the inverted commas I used there. Rock and roll careers, rock and roll pensions, investments in a rock and roll future – they are all around us. Ask Damon. Ask Noel). Mr Haines strummed a modest semi-acoustic in the Servants, mouthed a few back-up vocals and tinkled the odd ivory. The Master was in disguise – waiting to reveal himself. But by the time Mr Haines joined, the band was already nearing retirement. And when the Servants finally laid their last table in the rock and roll hotel, and made up their last bed, he removed his black jacket and tie, rolled up his Oxfam sleeves and took up residence in a room upstairs with his girlfriend Alice. He had begun writing his own songs.

It was not long before Mr Haines formed his own band, the Auteurs, with Alice on bass. He decided that he would only give himself one shot at success in his new venture – but that he would give it his all. If, having strained his every fibre and still failed, he would be forced to resort to his only other option – a career in journalism. Imagine that – all the blood amongst the shit.

But, of course, talent will out. And so Mr Haines jumped straight to the front of the queue of indie hopefuls – not very British but there you go – and got a record deal immediately. The record Mr Haines and the Auteurs made was called *New Wave*. It was *the* 'Britpop' album. Mr Haines had defined the genre before it even existed. The fellest of swoops.

At this point, at risk of us all having too much of a good thing, I offer up another quotation from William B:

> '... *an Angel at my birth*
> *Then said Descend thou upon earth*
> *Renew the Arts on Britain's Shore*
> *And France shall fall down and adore.*'

Mr Haines has always had a love/hate relationship with France. This is, of course, all part of being English. The French respect artists and thinkers more than the English do – although I believe that the mighty Vanessa Paradis has largely passed them by. The French loved the fact that Mr Haines called his band the Auteurs, apparently, but after the *New Wave* album they lost interest a little. Maybe it was the reference to cowboys in the title of his next opus – there is nothing very French about that, is there? Whereas the English are always fascinated to see what the colonials get up to during the course of their eternal exile from the promised land.

The estimable Jeremy Paxman comments in his book *The English: A Portrait of a People* that the English believe that no idea is worth dying for, whereas in the Paris Commune 45,000 French people died for one. The French do not understand the British. Mr Paxman informs us that all our sexual slang refers to them. Their 'sense of humour' is not attuned to irony. It is the same, of course, with the Americans.

Mr Haines made the following comment to me about *New Wave*:

'I was 24 years old when I made the record. This was my *New Wave*. It was a 'new wave' that other bands wanted to ride – even if that was due to a misinterpretation of 'American

Guitars' – Blur and the rest. And we were A NEW WAVE band. Nouvelle Vague indeed.'

'American Guitars', the song referred to above by Mr Haines, is about the balance of power between English and American rock music. The attention of *New Wave* as a whole is balanced between the two countries – Mr Haines exhibits here a fascination with America as well as an interest in the English class structure. Many of his early songs are fantasies about being raised up poor at the wrong end of American showbiz – the pull of the lights, the struggle to survive. America as the land of opportunity, Americana, an America seedy but romanticised.

'I hated England at the time of writing,' Mr Haines told me, tapping on the arm of his chair with the end of a finger. 'Why wouldn't I? The eighties had just ended – London was awful in the eighties. How the populace evaded mass suicide is beyond me.' He tapped a little harder. 'I had no money. I lived in Southgate, stuck at the end of the Piccadilly line, in a far too bohemian flat with a less than bohemian existence. I dreamt of New York and LA, having been to neither. It was as simple as that. The songs were the strongest hand.' He stopped tapping and brushed some imaginary dirt from his knee. 'I was aware that my personality would be perceived as 'difficult'. The *New Wave* songs were off-kilter with everything else around at the time. I wasn't bashful about using archaic language. Showgirls, vaudeville, innocent pastimes such as bowling.' He laughed. 'I was also quite puritanical at the time. Wouldn't let the other members of the band drink or smoke. Drugs were certainly not allowed.'

What, I ventured, did Mr Haines feel about bands who see themselves as gangs?

'Gang bands are crap,' he replied '– unless they really are sixteen-year-olds.'

And Mr Haines's own outfit?

'I always thought of it as more of an organisation or a cult. Maybe if my fanbase gets too small I can turn it into a real cult, and I'll become a David Koresh figure.'

At this point I mused aloud on why so little of Mr Haines's

writing of the time was autobiographical.

'I believe, he said, 'that the true artist reveals as little as possible of his psyche.'

Which reminded me of some advice that Oscar Wilde gave that most psychically attuned of painters, James Abbott McNeill Whistler:

'Be warned in time, James; and remain, as I do, incomprehensible. To be great is to be misunderstood.'

Whistler's family came from Goring on Thames. Upriver from Walton. There are certain parallels between him and Mr Haines. Whistler, too, was a contrarian. An accomplished arguer, quarreller and disagreer. And a misunderstood innovator. He was his own man. Whistler made no compromise in his art, he refused to bend the knee to public taste. 'Popularity is the only insult that has not yet been offered to Mr Whistler,' said Oscar Wilde. And then, of course, there was Whistler's famous public row with Ruskin which ended in Whistler being awarded a farthing in damages. The same Ruskin who conducted séances to try and contact the woman who had obsessed him since she was a child. The Ruskin whose wife, Effie, was taken from him by John Everett Millais, painter of 'Bubbles', that delightful evocation of childish innocence, a print of which hangs above the staircase in Myra and Billy's house.

Mr Haines's album *New Wave* was a huge success. Lauded and fêted throughout the land, across the Channel and even in the colonies! He recalled to me the time when he realised his own success:

'We were on tour. The album midweek was something like number twelve. It didn't really register with me. I wanted to move on with new stuff.'

Spoken like a true iconoclast!

In September '93, the annual Mercury Awards were handed out at London's Savoy Hotel. The Auteurs were nominated for 'best album' – but the judges gave the gong to Suede. Mr Haines must have felt like Whistler – who was distinctly unimpressed once at being awarded a 'second class' gold medal. In fact, Mr

Haines was both pissed up and mighty pissed off. So much so that he launched a fist in the direction of a member of the awards committee. Due to his inebriated state, however, the punch missed by a wide margin, making contact instead with a glass panel. Mr Haines was forced to seek the aid of the nearest Accident and Emergency unit. It was not just the prize about which he was miffed – he wanted the money, too. He needed it more than Suede did. When he found out later that they had donated their cheque to charity, he felt bad. In fact, he has since admitted that he quite likes them. What a gentleman Mr Haines is.

'Looking back,' I asked him, 'was it a good thing that you did not win the Mercury Prize?'

He snorted.

'In terms of merit it was the best album, so therefore it should have won. That being the point of the competition. The judges were vermin, pests – and they were the ones on our side. Given the history of the thing, not winning didn't do us any harm. I sleep OK at night.'

It was not only Suede, however, that Mr Haines managed to provoke. In December the Auteurs toured behind Matt Johnson's group The The. This arrangement had obviously been made arse-backwards and Mr Haines was further incensed when the Auteurs were asked to take third billing at one gig to a comedian. It all got quite nasty and resulted in Mr Haines removing his band from the rest of the tour. The incident got as far as a particularly slimy rag amongst the 'quality' press. Remove this copy from my nether regions immediately – I need an organ transplant. Aah, that's better – *The Guardian*. It offered Mr Haines editorial space to give his side of the dispute – but he could not see the point in 'slagging off pathetic independent bands' and so did not take up the paper's well-intentioned offer.

And now, if you will permit me to indulge myself a little, please turn the page for something that should have been.

An acceptance speech for the Mercury Award for Best Album of 1993:

'You were right – *New Wave* is the best album of this year. I just want to say thank you to all the little people in my life. You know who you are. I couldn't have done any of this without you to get my pizzas, clean my shoes and empty the bins. To me, you're all up here, too, sharing this award. In fact, if any of you want it, come and get it – just make sure you leave the cheque behind.

'To everyone who voted for me – don't expect me to be grateful, because I deserve it. And to the organisers – I look forward to being back here next year because I'm going to have the best album then, too. You might as well book me in now.

'You know what I think as I stand and look across this crowded room? I think the music industry is full of prats, twats, chancers, conmen and arseholes. It's all-inclusive, there's room for every kind of social deviant.

'I'd like to apologise if I've offended anyone here tonight – I know it's unlikely, but you never know there might be a sensitive soul in here somewhere. Trying to get out. Too many drugs, too much alcohol and not enough sex, I'm afraid. That's you lot, not me. Right, let's party. Which way to the cocaine, the champagne and the birds?'

Day Three

After breakfast today, I was invited down to the drawing room again for another performance. Two more actors have joined the cast – a man and a woman. Are they really doing all this just for me? Maybe there's going to be a play based on Haines's work – are they rehearsing? Perhaps I'm a sort of one-man preview audience? One of the new men is the spitting image of Haines. He did nothing, though – just looked on from the sidelines. The new woman is a darker haired version of Catherine.

Today it was scenes from the second Auteurs album, *I'm a Cowboy*. The actors were all decked out in smart sixties clothes: sharp suits with narrow collars and trousers for the men, knee-length skirts and tight polonecks for the women. It was like a mixture of *The Servant*, *Performance* and *Saturday Night and Sunday Morning* – on a shoestring. At the start the two women, Joanna and Margaret, were sitting next to each other at the front of the performing area, holding hands.

Joanna sighed. Margaret looked her in the eyes and said:

'It's wonderful that we're such good friends, darling, isn't it? For sisters. And lovers.'

Then Joanna rested her hand on Margaret's arm and said:

'Tell me how it happened.'

Margaret told the story of how the climbing trip taken by their brother, James, and his lover, Andrew, had ended in tragedy. Stranded on a snowy mountainside, the rescue team had found them twenty-four hours later – but too late to save Andrew, who was dead from exposure. James, recovering in his hospital bed, but traumatised after Andrew's death, had phoned Margaret – to tell her that his incestuous relationship with his two sisters was going to have to end.

'How's Mum taking it?' asked Joanna.

'Oh, you know,' said Margaret. 'She thinks she's being brave. But she's just shutting herself off. She believes it's God's will.'

The sisters each paused to wipe tears from their eyes.

'Oh, Joanna, what would I do without you?' Margaret said.

'Now that Andrew's gone, Margaret, we'll be like brothers. Blood brothers.'

The two actresses got up and were replaced by the two men from *New Wave*, who took their chairs and moved them further apart, twisting them so that they were opposite each other.

The older man had a handkerchief in his top pocket and a silk scarf draped round his neck. His hair had been side-parted and he kept flicking his fringe out of his eyes. The younger man was wearing eye-liner – he looked as though he had a pair of black eyes.

'Take it from me, baby boy,' said Paul, 'it's all a little more complicated than you think. You know what I should say to you? I should say "Go away, and come back – if I'll still have you – when you've found that out for yourself." When you've found out the meaning of the word "respect".'

He had moved his face close to James on that final word. James slowly wiped spit from his face before he spoke.

'Don't speak to me like that, Paul. There's nothing lacking in me. I'm not the one who feels incomplete. I'm not the one who's looking for something else. With someone else.'

'What would you know about it?' said Paul. 'How would you understand? You're just a little kid, watching the big boys. You'll learn. And then one day you'll be me. Then you'll understand.'

'I'll never understand you, Paul. I don't want to understand you. I don't want to know what makes you the way you are. I'd rather die not knowing.'

'Don't push it, James. It's cold outside. I wouldn't want to hear they'd found you slumped in a dooorway. Frozen on a doorstep. How would I ever forgive myself?'

'Don't, Paul, you know it upsets me.'

'Live with it, kiddy, you brought it on yourself. Spiteful little child. Daddy might just take away all your toys and give them to another little boy.'

The other actors were sitting on a line of chairs underneath the window, watching. The new guy was making notes. They kept their eyes on the two men the whole time – except for Catherine who, just once, flicked hers towards me.

The two men got up and walked over to the chairs. Paul handed his scarf to James. Paul picked up one of the chairs and moved it to the back of the room, while James removed his suit jacket, draped Paul's scarf round his neck and loosened his tie. Paul sat on the chair, lit up a cigarette and opened a bottle of whisky from the suitcase, pouring himself a glass. He sat cross-legged, drinking occasionally, smoking hard and, every now and then, twitching. He didn't say a word over the next scene, just watched.

James sat down on his chair and then the new actor got up from his place, picked up another chair and put it alongside James's.

'How's it going, James?' he said.

'Oh – you know.'

'That bad?'

James laughed, but it was more like a shudder.

'Does he trust you?' asked the other man.

James laughed again – and this time it came from high up in his throat.

'No, Harry, he doesn't trust me. I don't think he even likes me any more.'

'Well – whenever you're ready.' He looked around him, his eyes travelling up and down the walls of the drawing room. 'Just say the word.'

'No. It's not like that. I don't want it to be like that.'

'It is like that, James. It'll always be like that.' He grinned. 'It'll be like the old days. Only this time we'll know we're not going to get caught.'

'I thought that was why you did it, Harry, for the risk?'

'Well, priorities change, James. You'll learn that. I guess you could call it maturity. I'll sacrifice the kicks for the money. That's kind of what I'm concentrating on now. The money. A career path. Less excitement but more long-term security. And while we're on the subject, have you got something for me? Because I have something for you.'

He smiled and tapped his pocket. James reached into his.

James handed Harry the money. Harry responded with a small packet that James slid inside his jacket.

Harry stood up. He pointed to a painting on the wall opposite – I think it was the first Earl's wife.

'Bet we could get a few quid for that.'

James twitched. Behind him, Paul stared vacantly at him. Then James got up and began to usher Harry across the floor.

Harry went willingly enough, but he paused by the door.

'You could go away, James. Wherever you want. And wherever you were, I'd come and visit you.'

'The trust fund, Harry. The trust fund.'

Harry laughed.

'Okay, James, believe that a little longer if it makes you happy. But not too long. Just remember – call me before he kicks you out, not after. A couple of days is all we'll need.'

The other actors got up from their chairs then and James, Paul and Harry replaced theirs. Then the whole cast began to file off down the room, eyes fixed on the door again – except for Catherine. She flashed a brief smile in my direction.

Before I left the room, I checked the catches on the bottom windows. No problems there.

I wandered over to the dining room after the performance and poured myself a coffee from the silver urn, added cream from the white jug with the curled lip and some brown sugar from the gold jar. I glanced up at the portrait of the first Earl. There's a sadness in his face. Imprisoned inside that fat, self-centred man, maybe there was a thinner, more sensitive one.

The bell again – lunch – but the ringing shorter, less forceful and less rhythmical.

The food was served by the maid. No actors. No Stevenson. And nothing lined up for the afternoon. Back upstairs then.

Reading an old interview, I pictured Haines at home as a kid, watching reruns of *The Persuaders* alone on his parents' black and white TV. Adventures of an English aristocrat born into money and an American slum kid who got it the hard way – old world class and new world glamour. Haines lusting after both and dreaming mythic dreams.

Staring out of the window, I saw one of the gardeners in the distance, wheeling a barrow with a spade slung across it. He stopped, picked up the spade, lifted it high and brought it down hard on something. Then he carried on his way again. The sound of crows and wood pigeons.

Supper. No Stevenson again – I haven't seen him all day.

Back upstairs. Writing this. It's late now. All quiet. No strange noises outside. I'm going out.

I went down the stairs and opened the door at the bottom, just like before. Down past the kitchens – the hum of fridges and freezers, tiny red power switches glowing deep inside the darkness. No Stevenson this time to flood the place with light and scare the shit out of me. I made it to the end of the corridor and into the entrance hall.

You can feel the history, walking through here at night – the ghosts hanging in the air. Soldiers, lords, ministers, passing through, casting their spells on the marble and granite. Halfway along I stopped and whispered a name. The sound flew up to the ceiling like a trapped bird.

I left the hall and began to pad along the wooden corridor the other side. It's dead sound down there – your footsteps sink into the wood and vanish. I turned the handle of the drawing room door, which glided open as smoothly as the day it was hung. I stared into the darkness. Tiny hints of gold from the frames of the paintings. And a faint glow from the corner of the windows down at the far end – the light from the carriage lamp by the north entrance filtering over. I stumbled once on my way across the floor. Some idiot had left a chair in the middle.

I unlocked the window and slid it open. Almost immediately I heard the sound of an owl. The full moon was high – bright, round and white in a mass of black sky. I climbed on to the window sill. I could smell the thick resin of pine needles on the breeze. I dropped to the ground.

I crossed over the lawn, stopping halfway to look back. No lights in the windows of the Hall. Even the carriage lamps were already less bright, like eyes beginning to close. I turned right along the path that I had driven down with Stevenson the previous day, walking fast along the loose stones, but looking around me all the time for any signs of life. Thick, dark woods near the arch. Once I was out of sight of the house, I slowed down. The trees grew taller, the path lengthened, the grass on either side widened. The air seemed to settle. On my left beech trees replaced the pine. Ahead in the distance, on the far side of the darkened light aircraft, there were grand oaks. Thirty yards to my right there were yew trees – and hidden behind them somewhere was the churchyard. I stopped and stared at the yews. There was a hint of light coming from there. I began to cross the grass towards it. Soon I was passing behind the statue of the kid in the lamé jacket. His shirt-tail is hanging out of his trousers. The grass was soft and dark. Suddenly I stopped.

It was twenty years ago. And I was back at home. It was the night after Jessica died.

The middle of that night. And I was reaching up to undo the latch on the back door. And then I was standing in the garden in bare feet. The grass so cool and soft. The night spread out around me. Holding me, asleep inside it.

And then it was the next morning. And I was waking up as normal, back in bed. And at breakfast Mum told Dad that she had heard the back door closing in the night.

The light was coming from a small outbuilding in the trees. There was a track leading through the woods towards it, semi-overgrown as if it was only occasionally used. As I got closer, I could see the window of a small cottage in a clearing. As I came clear of the last couple of trees, I saw it standing there – tiny, plump and white with two windows, a door with a brass knocker and a roof of red slate with a black chimney pot like an upended liquorice allsort. I crept towards the window. There was a figure deep inside the room, with his back towards me. Skirting the front of the house, I looked round the window frame. The window was cracked and the room was shabby. An old sofa, sunken and worn, a dresser with open drawers, their sides loose or missing. The figure was Haines, paintbrush in hand, in front of an easel. With one eye looking round the slat of peeling wood, I watched him. He didn't move. After thirty seconds, I shifted until I was right in front of the window. And then I realised that no, it wasn't Haines – it was a waxwork dummy. On a couch set against the far wall a naked woman was reclining – another waxwork. Her ragged clothes were in a pile on the floor. There were black and blue marks on her skin – dark bruises, too exaggerated to be real. She was near middle age, with a hint of roundness to her stomach. Her hair was a mess. In the picture Haines was painting, though, he had made her young again – slim-waisted, fresh-faced, clear-skinned. I turned away from the window. Perfectly framed through the trees was the distant statue of the kid.

I walked back towards it and ahead a shooting star faintly burned and crashed. As I came closer I heard a weird noise in the distance. I stopped and listened. It was the same noise I had heard the night before – and it was getting louder. I made for the pedestal of the statue – and crouched down low behind it. Now I could see the arch leading to the eastern colonnade of the Hall. From underneath it a weird troupe of figures was emerging on to the path, heading towards the aircraft. They were howling, yelping and screaming – unearthly, bloodcurdling noises. A couple of them had torches that rippled fire up into the air, casting strange shadows on to stranger faces – masked, hooded and furred. As they came closer I heard baboon-like gibbers, and roars, too. And then they drew level with me. As I stared between the legs of the kid, I could see red eyes, bloodied claws and cloven feet. They stopped in front of the aircraft and one of the creatures swung itself up on to the undercarriage. Reaching up, it stretched a finger on to the fuselage and pressed a button. Immediately the cockpit filled with red light. I could see the features of the crashing airman inside, anguished and terrified, while the familiar plumes of black smoke began to funnel into the sky. The beast leapt off the aircraft and bounced up and down on the ground like a chimpanzee while the other members of the crew gathered round, applauding and staring up at the fire and smoke, jeering and screeching at the falling flyer. Then a strange chant came up from them. After a few seconds, I realised that it was a rendition of one of Haines's songs – 'X-Boogie Man'. After a few rounds of this they got bored and moved off eastwards, howling and leaping as they went. They grew smaller and quieter with the distance and then I saw them leave the path and cut across the open ground towards the wood. Passing into the trees, the last of them paused, hurled his torch up into the air and caught it again expertly like a drum major. Then finally they were gone and I was left staring at the trapped pilot in his blazing metal cabin.

I felt a strange sort of pity for that figure imprisoned in the aircraft. I walked across the grass towards it. Stopping in front of the plane, I looked up. Against the black of the sky behind, the red seemed brighter and fiercer, while against the red the pilot's suffering seemed more intense. He seemed to be burning in his own private hell. I pulled myself up on to the carriage and reached up to the fuselage, as the creature had done – and pushed the same button. I put out the flames that were tormenting the airman. The interior of the cabin was dark again now, but I hoped that the expression on his face was peaceful.

I made my way back to the house. Slipping back through the drawing room window, I closed it behind me and retraced my steps, up to my bed.

Editor's note —

Well, I say, what on earth is going on here? The writer seems to be losing it – already.

And oh dear, look at the pitiful length of this piece. He seems, despite everything, not to have had very much to say for himself today. No matter, we shall use the opportunity to improve the balance of the book by dealing further with the life and career of Mr Haines.

But first let us return to the beginning of the writer's apparently impoverished day.

He is right to question the reason for the actors' performances. Obviously what is being presented to him is not being presented *for* him. But no, there is to be no play. And no, these are not rehearsals – not for the writer, anyway. They are part of the reality in which he has found himself.

The writer – before he goes all weird on us – claims to have detected a certain melancholy in the portrait in the dining hall of the first Earl. He sees a ghostly vision of a rather gaunt individual imprisoned within those chubby cheeks and that tub-like torso. I will go with that. It is my belief that this gaunt individual found true expression only during the hours that the Earl spent among the large collection of dead beasts, plucked from every continent and from land, sea and air, which he kept in a glass house in the winter garden.

Let me give a brief account of the first Earl's life. He was a collector of all manner of flora, fauna and minerals – not to mention paintings, statuary and a wide variety of other antiquary. He believed that his riches came from God – that he had been granted them by divine right, and that they were his to dispose of in any way he saw fit, no matter how selfish and greedy that disbursement might be seen by anyone else. But what God delivers, He can also take away. The Earl's laziness led him to entrust his financial affairs to a local solicitor with a stern manner, an efficient stride and the neatest of handwriting. Unbeknownst to the Earl, this man soon began to divert the profits from his employer's Jamaican estates into his own tightly stitched pockets. Meanwhile, at home, in the name of sound investment, estates were sold cheaply to the mountebank's associates, while others were bought at inflated prices, with a large commission finding its way into the same upper parts of his breeches. When, after eighteen months, this adviser abruptly left the Earl's employ, claiming that the sudden and tragic death of his widowed sister had left him no option but to leave immediately for the remote Scottish island she had inhabited, where he would now need to devote himself to the care of her five orphaned children, the Earl was sad to see him go. Sadness turned, however, to rage and then despair once his next financial adviser revealed the extent of his predecessor's embezzlement. Needless to say, the forwarding address in Scotland turned out to be fictitious. The Earl ordered his new adviser to sell, to mortgage, to borrow, and to raise the rents of the tenant farmers on his many estates – anything that might rescue his dire financial situation. The adviser embarked on this toughest of campaigns, remarking that the Earl's noble belt, too, might need to be tightened. The Earl responded that the size of his girth had been ordained by God and no man was entitled to reduce it. Eventually, after an extended period of financial reorganisation and the unfortunate but necessary reduction of the tenant farmers to a new level of penury, the honest and hard-working adviser succeeded in his task, and bankruptcy was averted. The price of this victory, though, was the creation of a trust to run the Earl's affairs, and the ceding of control of the Hall and the estate to his despised son. The Earl retired to his conservatory and spent the rest of his days in the company of his animals, alive and dead. He was buried next to his faithful hound, Marmaduke.

Returning to the actors, it is interesting to see the way that their performance is developing – to see the various exercisings of power between older and younger and rich and poor, and between and within the sexes. And there are not just thieves now but uber-thieves, too.

In the light of the sparring here between James and Paul it is worth noting that in one version of Bryan Forbes's screenplay for *Seance on a Wet Afternoon* the central relationship was between a homosexual medium and his younger lover.

The night-time exploration is an interesting departure for the writer – I say this because I have no way of knowing if any of it really happened. There is nothing either to confirm or deny it. You will notice a 'story-telling' tone creeping into his narrative. The description of the 'cottage' – it is really no more than an 'outbuilding' – is bizarrely fanciful. Perhaps, his nerve having failed him, he decided to invent an episode that would cover up his cowardice?

But then perhaps the writer really did escape from his chains on this night? Perhaps he had a kind of waking nightmare? He does, after all, describe a childhood sleepwalking incident as a prelude to it. Well, if he really was out there, late at night, near the church, amongst the yew trees, all I can say is that it is a good thing he did not stumble into the old lean-to garage next to the outbuilding in the churchyard. He might have lifted a mossy tarpaulin to discover a sleepy old Cortina.

There is a song on *Now I'm a Cowboy* entitled 'Life Classes/ Life Model'. I assume the writer has been listening to it. Mr Haines has described it as the most brutal song on the record. It concerns an artist and his model and is autobiographical. How sweet – and puzzling – that the writer should, within this scenario, see Mr Haines bestowing the gift of youth on a middle-aged lady.

Another song on this record is called 'Daughter of a Child'. It concerns the disappearance of a girl. It is the first of Mr Haines's songs to deal with a murder, and it takes the point of view of the killer.

Mr Haines's song 'X-Boogie Man' appeared on the B-side of the 'Light Aircraft on Fire' single. The creatures portrayed within its bars are bogie men, Hammer horrors, bestial kidnappers, Genghis Khans and Jack the Rippers, murderers and abusers of the innocent. They are like the creatures locked underground in that Lovecraft story, underneath the farm of Curwen, Ward's ancestor. Strange sounds, chantings and screams come from the tunnels down there, below the lights that burn all night long – and Curwen orders extra meat and fresh blood from the local butcher.

There are parallel lines that can be traced through Mr Haines's early B-sides. They are like a series of sub-texts that only emerge into the open on the later A-sides and the albums. On the flip-sides of the singles from *Now I'm a Cowboy* Mr Haines gets into a new strain of writing that only makes it out into the open on *After Murder Park* – and then finally erupts on *Baader Meinhof*. Aberrant behaviour, drugs, arson, terrorism.

That sort of thing.

Well, we seem to have drifted back towards the real story – that of the career of Mr Haines. All well and good. With the writer still struggling vainly to bring himself into the great man's presence, we should return to my own more successful attempt to converse with him. But first a little more background.

After the success of *New Wave*, Mr Haines's record company – it goes without saying – requested more of the same. And fast. Mr Haines, ever the obliging sort, gave it to them. *Now I'm a Cowboy*. His one mistake, he reckons now. What he should have done was immediately to destroy his own creation. Well, he would not be human if he had not erred once, would he?

It was spring of '94 before *Now I'm a Cowboy* was released – its arrival coinciding with the launch of *Loaded* 'magazine'. Football, beer, birds and Oasis. Damon Albarn as a 'mockney' 'new lad'. Mr Haines must have felt in good company. The title of his record can be interpreted as 'Now I can be whatever I want'. An understandable bit of hubris after the massive success of *New Wave*. *Cowboy* is a more cynical record than its predecessor. All its scenarios – as opposed to just some of them – are twisted or skewed.

Part of the plan to promote it was a tour supporting Nirvana, but this had to be cancelled as the unfortunate Kurt Cobain was on the path that would soon lead to his tragic suicide. Mr Haines liked Nirvana. Indeed he has been uncharacteristically fulsome in his praise of them. It would have been an interesting tour. Maybe they will do it in heaven one day. But not just yet.

Right, we are back in Mr Haines's salon. The two of us are stretched out on our chairs. I lift my head. What, I ponder aloud, inspired the songs on *Now I'm a Cowboy*?

'Those songs were born out of class tourism experienced first hand within the music business,' he replied. 'I believed at the time that class divisions should be re-established – that the lower classes should work in service to the upper classes. The aristocracy should be abolished as they were just a bunch of scions of Tudor accountants, arselickers of nobility.'

Yes. Mr Haines begins on this record to equate the upper classes with the 'bosses' of the music industry. He resents the head honchos. He wants the kind of power they have over careers. There are songs here about experience, and about age taking advantage of youth and innocence. Songs about masters and servants. Add some of the distortions and cross-cutting of Mr Bob Dylan on *Highway 61 Revisited* and *Blonde on Blonde* and you have something really rather interesting.

'I was accused of being middle class,' Mr Haines continued. 'Not so. Both parents from working class stock. One car, one income as a civil servant (until my mother trained to be a teacher when I was fifteen). Technically, this makes me upper working class. I do not believe the working class are honourable, I am just a stickler for the facts. I noticed that the music industry was one of the few places where one can rub shoulders with anyone from any class, e.g. Blair inviting pop stars to Downing Street in 1997. Justine Frischman* noticed this. So did Pulp.'

My question about the inspiration for *Now I'm a Cowboy* seemed to have led us close to the edge of what might be a political minefield. Mr Haines's new landed status seems to have made him defensively proletarian. I decided to change tack. How did he go about presenting himself in the live arenas of the capital?

He jerked upright.

'I decided that the songs would have to sell themselves,' he replied. 'We had no money.' He chuckled at the memory. 'Our stage attire consisted of one horrible crushed velvet smoking jacket that I walked around each and every day in.' He paused to finger the silk lining of his current, more upmarket version. 'And a pile of wing-collar shirts from Oxfam, the sort I'd been buying since I was fifteen. None of this was any particular 'style' statement, these were just the clothes that you could afford that didn't look that terrible. I was right. Played through the shoddy PA systems of the capital's worst venues, the songs did actually sell themselves.'

'Having lurked in the wings, so to speak, in the Servants,' I said, 'how did you feel about stepping out from the shadows and taking the spotlight?'

'Yeah, I was OK,' he responded good-humouredly. 'The job had to be done. I knew I was gonna maybe go into some previously uncharted frontman territories. Early on there was a contradiction between my sometimes taciturn nature and a desire for confrontation with the audience. It meant that a lot of the early gigs were both confrontational and brutal. I remember them fondly.'

At this point he sank back with what – if I did not know better – I would have said was a nostalgic sigh.

'A lot of the Johnny-come-latelies were expecting a fey, bookish Lloyd Cole* thing,' he continued. 'What they actually got was an English Nirvana, albeit with better songs, and a singer coming out on stage slow-clapping the audience and performing half the set a cappella as the ancient equipment failed. That is entertainment.'

Mr Haines poured himself a whisky – more like a double, actually. He waved the bottle at me half-heartedly but I demurred. With Mr Haines a refusal never offends.

I asked my host for his first impressions of the United States, and how the band was received. In April '93 the Auteurs played their first dates on the dark side of the pond – and made a return trip the following year. 'Dogged and colourless,' pooh-poohed the *LA Times*, 'sometimes intriguing... often so-so,' sniffed the *San Francisco Chronicle*.

'I've always liked LA,' said Mr Haines charitably. 'It's an ideal place to be an Englishman. Not as vapid as people would have you think, eccentric, but still with plenty to moan about. American audiences didn't know what to make of us, they thought we were trying to be beatniks. The first US tour was fractious. I sacked the tour manager halfway through.' Mr Haines's chin was jutting out now. He tapped the arm of the chair twice. 'I wasn't used to Americans and found him irritating,' he said. Now he was scratching at the arm of the chair, as if at some invisible stain. 'He said we were like a Monty Python sketch,' he continued, 'in that annoying way that some Americans do. Calling the Brits 'tea bags' etc.'

But how about the East Coast? What about New York? How juicy was the Big Apple, how receptive to the Hainesian bite? The American-flavoured songs on *Now I'm a Cowboy* are about the worthlessness of celebrity and the necessity of true artistic endeavour. Mr Haines is ruthless about anything that is past its sell-by-date. It is the only way to be. When one reaches this condition one must be removed from the store – for the benefit of all consumers. Mr Haines talks about the Warhol scene in New York, about the poets, the underground movies and the music, but he locates all this firmly in the past. Times have changed, he says. Mr W's Factory has been swept with a new broom – and that instrument of change belongs to Mr Haines. In a delightful song entitled 'Brainchild' an older artist is threatened by a younger one, whom he accuses of stealing his ideas. The whole sixties lower-east-side legacy is being milked by people who are unable to think on their own, Mr Haines says. They are graverobbers selling rotting remains.

'When we first went to New York,' he informed me enigmatically, 'the city was still fun. All the bad people were still roaming around.'

Enough said, sir!

After returning from the second US trip, the Auteurs recorded the incendiary 'Light Aircraft on Fire'. By now Mr Haines had ended his exile in Southgate and was living in a more central location – Camden. On his arrival here he had found the area already well-populated with pop stars. In fact, he could barely set foot fom his pad without falling over their prostrate forms: Morrissey, Blur, Oasis, all genuflecting horribly. 'Camden's great,' Mr Haines has opined. 'It's full of drunks. Drunks and beggars.'

With the 'Aircraft' session in the bag, the Auteurs set off on a European tour. Stage one of Mr Haines's career – as a voyeuristic, cynical dabbler and paranoid, vengeful, class-obsessed commentator – was drawing to a close.'

By September '94 things were looking very good – the singles had been doing excellent business, the European tour was a sell-out, sycophantic headlines filled the music press. Next stop the world. Well, Japan anyway – booked solid for a money-spinning, product-promoting tour. But then our hero became somewhat inebriated one night in Spain and jumped off a wall – breaking both his ankles. Yes – he looked fame long and hard in the eye, took careful aim and spat. The fall resulted in a major operation and the cancellation of the rest of the European tour. And that visit to the Far East.

There followed three months in a wheelchair. In which Mr Haines was forced to witness Blur picking up 'best album' at the 'Q' awards and Oasis getting 'best new (sic) act'. Not to mention Tony Blair making a speech. And, of course, there was the fact that Britpop – which apparently did not include the Auteurs, despite the fact that Mr Haines had actually created it with *New Wave* – was sweeping the nation. Mr Haines's standard line after the accident was that he had done it on purpose as a way of getting out of his record contract. This was a good tale but, of course, total bollocks.

'What was the story behind you jumping off the wall?' I asked – rather directly.

He sighed good-naturedly.

'We were halfway through a long European tour, having just toured the UK and US. I didn't travel well and was unhappy with some of the company I was forced to keep. I began deliberately alienating myself from the rest of the tour party. I think the problem was that, apart from Alice (who was under a lot of pressure from exasperating behaviour) I felt I was spending too many days in the company of paid employees whom I didn't actually like. I just drank too much cheap sangria on a night off in San Sebastian. Tried to take a short cut back to the hotel. Underestimated the height of the wall – fifteen feet – and misjudged what I was going to land on. Concrete not sand.'

Thank you for your candour, sir. As Mr Haines had mentioned Alice, I thought I would try and draw him out a little on the subject of girls – just a little harmless background stuff, nothing too personal. One for the ladies. He once said that while in the Auteurs he never wrote a single love song. An admirable boast! To quote Mr John Rotten, 'Love is something you feel for a dog or a pussy cat' – and therefore of no interest to the true artist.

'Do you remember anything of interest about your early girlfriends?' I asked jauntily. 'What kind of girls did you 'go for'?'

He smiled easily.

'Art school girls with dyed black or blonde hair,' he said. 'Punky art school girls. Girls in art school who owned Nico* albums. Older art school girls who liked Iggy and the Stooges*. Girls at school liked me, but they probably thought I was a sissy for liking stupid music and wearing stupid clothes. The only thing about going to art school as a precocious sixteen-year-old was those older art school girls.'

Art school – that, of course, had been in Portsmouth. Sadly one cannot choose the environments to which one is sometimes dragged while below the age of majority.

'For how long did you attend this establishment?' I enquired.

'One year. I got asked to leave after that.'

'Why was that?'

'For having a bad attitude to further education. I spent most of my time there waiting for the Viennese 'action' group* to roll up – I didn't realise that they were mainly all incarcerated on various vice charges. That and trying to find hallucinogenic plants in the local Botanical Gardens. To no success but only one serious case of poisoning.' He sighed. 'Like good records, drugs were also hard to come by in the early eighties.'

'Did you want to be a painter?' I asked gently.

Mr Haines had painted the cover of the Servants' album *Disinterest* – and an estimable piece of work it is, too. He is also known for his strident views on 'Britart', which for him occupies a similar level in the cultural heap to Britpop.

'I didn't take it remotely seriously,' he answered after a judicious pause. 'I was only there to avoid reality. Sadly most people there were embracing the witless drudge reality of the time, walking around trying to look like Robert Smith*. My painting skills are sadly not up to much. I never honed it, and by then was more interested in conceptualists – as opposed to conceptual artists.'

Mr Haines certainly is opposed to conceptual artists – he wrote a song about one called 'I Shot Sarah Lucas' and seems to particularly relish performing it in public. Maybe on the off chance that her 'spirit' is in the room, come to examine the murderer's motivation.

'Which artists did you admire?' I asked. The true answer to this may well be 'None' but I had caught Mr Haines in generous mood.

'I always liked the Vorticists*,' he replied, 'though at the time Wyndham Lewis was deeply unfashionable and still remembered, if at all, as a Nazi apologist. The Dadaists knocked the Surrealists into a cocked hat. You've always got to go back to the source. Situationists over Reid/Westwood/ McLaren*. Viennese 'action' over Coum/TG*. And the Industrial Revolution over the Futurists*.'

Well, I asked for it!

'What about Portsmouth itself,' I wondered, 'did you manage to find anything at all of interest there?'

'Helen Duncan was successfully prosecuted under the Witchcraft Act,' he said, 'for holding a séance above a shop. She received a custodial sentence in 1949. The last person to be tried under the Witchcraft Act in this country.'

He sounded like a guide on some occult tour of the south coast! Mr Haines has written about Crowley in Hastings, of course. And there is the séance in 'Unsolved Child Murder'. And... but let us not get ahead of ourselves.

Well, thank you, sir. We shall leave it there for today.

But before we end we must squeeze in a few footnotes by way of explanation:

*Justine Frischman, leader of Elastica. The indie Posh Spice. She had her Becks, too, for a while – Damon from Blur.

*Lloyd Cole. Songs in the style of Bob Dylan, Lou Reed and Tom Verlaine.

* Nico. Blonde acting-school girl who briefly fronted the Velvet Underground.

* Iggy and the Stooges. Iggy – a proto-Haines with a rather more lively stage presence. Mr Haines would refuse the opening-up-your-chest-with-a-broken-bottle act, too – self-abuse really should not be painful.

*The Viennese 'action' group. A deranged club of dieting enthusiasts who attempted to take action against the terrible obesity of the various species of Teutonic cow by removing large sections of their intestines and flinging them at each other live on stage. Their show was also intended as a terrible warning to the bovine members of their audiences about the perils of insane greed. Hermann Nitsch – the bullock's bollocks.

*Robert Smith. Lead singer of pop group The Cure, beefy, cow-eyed, fond of ruminatory poses… Watch out, Bob, they're coming to get you.

*In the Vorticist magazine *Blast* there were lists of the 'blasted' and the 'blessed' – a device Malcolm McLaren used later with the Sex Pistols and one that Mr Haines would adapt for the booklet of his record *The Oliver Twist Manifesto*.

*Reid/Westwood/McLaren – Jamie, Vivienne and Malcolm. A sort of punk Peter Paul and Mary.

*Coum/TG. GenesisPorridgeThrobbingGristleartystuff.

*The Futurists. Style to the Industrial Revolution's content.

Day Four

It was Stevenson who woke me today. Apparently the maid had knocked earlier but hadn't been able to get a reply and had left me to sleep. Stevenson was not so considerate. He may have knocked, I don't know, but all I remember is waking up suddenly as the door was flung open and he came flying in. I sat bolt upright, but he went straight past me to the window and pulled the curtains apart.

'We really must try and pull ourselves together, mustn't we, sir?' he said. 'Time waits for no man and today is going to be a busy day.' He picked up the jeans I had left on the floor and put them on a chair. Then he clapped his hands. 'Breakfast finishes in eight minutes. I suggest you attend, sir, otherwise you will have to make do with the cup of tea that Mary left outside your door forty-five minutes ago and which may now be a trifle on the chilly side.'

He left the door open. So the maid's name was Mary.

I made it down to the dining hall in time to grab a piece of rubbery toast and a cup of grainy, gritty coffee.

Stevenson's attitude seemed to have changed. He was still calling me 'sir' but the new sarcasm was an unwelcome new element. Maybe yesterday had been a bad day? Where had he been? Maybe in town visiting an upmarket caterer's, ordering a selection of food appropriate for the table of an aristocrat? Maybe attending some butlering convention somewhere? Maybe he had been with Haines. Where is Haines?

I wondered what Stevenson meant by a busy day. I had it in mind that this was another piece of sarcasm and that we would probably amble around another part of the grounds for an hour or two before returning for lunch. But it wasn't to work out quite like that.

There's an Auteurs single called 'Back With the Killer Again' which came out after *Now I'm a Cowboy*. It's a savage piece of work about a man who takes drugs to turn himself into a murderer – and has a boy for an accomplice. I was soon to meet them both.

As soon as I got back to my room after breakfast I was ordered downstairs again – by Mary. I heard her knock this time. She handed me a card saying: 'Main entrance 09.15' and then, with a slip of the head and a dip of her waist she was gone. I had five minutes. After a quick shave – I think I had some idea that Stevenson might be less sharp with me if I smartened myself up a bit – I went down.

When I got to the entrance hall, the main door was open. Through it I could see a US army jeep, motor running, exhaust fumes puffing from its rear. The smell of burnt petrol was invading the hall. I went out, pulling the door closed behind me. Standing next to the jeep, arms clasped behind his back, legs apart, mirror shades like dark-glass bubbles on his face, was a GI. There was no sign of Stevenson. In the driver's seat was a kid – maybe fourteen years old – wearing dark glasses, too. Next to him was a crewcut tattooed man whose breath rasped as he inhaled from a mask that he was holding against his face with one hand. In the back there were two men in anti-contamination suits, their faces enclosed in rubber breathing masks, strapped heavily into their seats. The back door of the jeep was open and I walked towards it, waiting for the two men to move so that I could get in. But they didn't – because they couldn't. They were dummies. With wide-open, blood-ringed eyes. I turned to the GI and had just started to mouth a question when I found myself picked up and shoved on to the knees of the plastic passengers in the back seat. The door shut behind me and then, in a cloud of dust, the Kid accelerated away towards the arch. The blue sky flashed and blurred above, around and then beneath me as I tumbled on to the floor.

All I saw of the arch as we passed through was its underside. I was lying in the well of the jeep, struggling to sit up, fighting the vicious jolts from the road. Once I'd made it into an upright position I managed to wedge myself into the gap between the false legs of the two dummies. I could feel the material of their suits slipping across the smooth plastic underneath. The Kid was grinning as he looked across at the Killer, who just kept pulling on his gas and wheezing. With his other hand he was holding on to the windshield, his arm locked tight like the spar of a bridge. The Kid left the road then and began to drive parallel with it, bumping across the grass, with dirt flying up from the wheels, sending us all lurching up and down. The little tit was whooping, too. Then he suddenly hammered the wheel to the left and yanked on the handbrake. In a hail of grass, dirt, mud and gravel we slid back across the road and then on to a track I hadn't noticed before. We were heading into the wood. The trees flashed by on either side as we crashed through the undergrowth. And then the Kid slammed on the brakes, the wheels locked and we skidded to a halt.

We were in a clearing. In front of us was a dark, unmarked warehouse, sheer panels rising up to an asymmetrical roof. The scrub had been sawn and scissored back a few yards on each side, but the trees climbed high behind that line, parallel with the walls. The Kid was out of the jeep immediately and so was the Killer, who reached for me with one hand, the other still clamped to his face, and hauled me out, too. Somehow I managed not to lose my footing completely, staggering a couple of paces before pulling myself upright again. The Killer came up behind and shoved me towards the warehouse – but I was prepared for that. I kept going, barely missing a stride this time. Then the three of us were standing in front of a door in the building and I was staring up at the wall. It stretched up into the sky, steep, black, ribbed. The Killer was peeling open the heavy metal door as if he was opening a sardine tin.

Inside, the darkness was deepened by the silence. All I could make out in front of me was the shape of another wall and a skeletal staircase. And then the Killer dragged the door shut behind us and it became darker still. Like deep space. For a second nothing happened. Then he grabbed me by the elbow and dragged me towards the staircase. I didn't struggle – because I had no choice, I was blind. There was no way of running, nowhere to hide. His strength said that he knew what he was doing and where he was going – all I could do was follow. Then he shoved me forward and I was sent sprawling on to the iron stairs. There were holes in the metal – I hooked on to them with my fingers. And then I picked myself up and started climbing. They were invisible cold grids, those stairs, angled, pushing me up towards the roof. The Killer's boots clanged on the steps behind me, rhythmical and loud, like the beat of an industrial noise band. They pushed me higher. In between the stamping of his feet, he hauled air into his chest. I could almost feel his ribcage vibrating with the effort.

We came to a bend in the staircase and then we were moving round to the right. We must have been moving parallel with the wall of the warehouse. Then we moved forward again. I was holding on to the rail as we went so when I stepped forward and found my right hand meeting only air I was able to lurch round to the left and grab on with that hand, too. For a split second I was sure I was stepping into empty space – falling off the edge of the world – but then I was slipping and bumping and falling down no more than half a dozen steps on to some kind of platform. Even as I fell I heard the regular metallic stomp of the Killer behind me – his stride didn't break.

I was sore and shaken, but I picked myself up again and found that there was a guard rail in front of me. I clung on to it. I realised that we must be on the other side of the massive, dark wall that I had stared up at from outside. Up high, with the rafters somewhere close to our heads. I still couldn't see a thing, not even a pinprick of light, not a tiny hint of an alteration in the blackness in front of me. The footsteps of the Killer had come up close behind me, but then they had veered off to the left, before falling silent. I could hear his breathing but it was quieter and more controlled. He was standing still somewhere in the darkness.

Suddenly the silence was filled with screaming sound. I flung my hands up to my ears, trying to cover them against the shrieking, trying to blot out the murderous noise – of an aircraft engine fighting for control as a plane plummeted from the sky. And then the darkness, too, was blown apart – by a blinding white light and the searing red light of fire. Barely a couple of yards in front of me, clamped to the framework of an iron gantry, was the blazing cabin of another light aircraft on fire. In the pilot's seat was the actor who looks like Haines. He was dressed in a World War Two flying helmet, and had a thin, dark moustache. This time, though, the second figure in the cabin was different – black-cloaked, wide-hatted, dog-collared. It was the actor who had played Paul. Both men wore headphones. As well as the noise of the aircraft I could hear two voices, in stereo, a radio conversation – one was male, ranting and aggressive, the other female, pleading and anguished. The male voice was coming from the preacher. He was screaming about faith, betrayal and damnation. The woman's voice was bathed in static, but she was offering up love, despair and sex. The actor playing Haines sat immobile, not even his eyes moved.

'They'll revenge themselves on you,' the preacher was screaming. 'They'll send you to hell, burn you, flay you, disembowel you. Torment you, torture you, trash you, torch you.'

'Do it for me, darling,' countered the woman. 'Come back to me, lover. I love you, I need you, I want you. Bring it on back, bring it on home, see me, feel me, fill me.

'They'll fry your brains in your own shit,' ranted the preacher. 'They'll string you and hole you. They'll bathe in your blood and eat your ears.'

'Ride with me, darling,' urged the woman, 'drive me. Fly with me, put me on your wings, we'll float up to heaven, up to the stars.'

And then – as suddenly as it had started – it stopped. Noise, light. Everything. Gone. As if it had all been sucked in to a black hole.

And then I was blind again in the darkness and the silence,

in that vaccuum of light and sound, and standing holding my numbed head in my hands. The Killer grabbed me and manhandled me back on to the staircase and then down – and then along the horizontal section and down again. With one hand on the rail to steady me, I moved down the metal stairs as fast as I could in the dark, waiting for a boot in the back that never came. And then, finally, we were at the bottom and the Killer was in front of me again and hauling me back through that door, back out into the sunlight, and my hands flew to my eyes to stop the light piling into my head. As the warehouse door clanged shut behind me I knew he would be gunning for me again, forcing me back into the jeep, so I opened my eyes and shook my head and did his job for him. I staggered there myself. The Kid was lounging against the jeep's bonnet, smoking a cigarette. He smirked as I climbed into the back seat.

We drove off again, back the way we had come, fast and furious. I thought we were heading back to the Hall and inside me something lifted, but then the Kid hung a left down another track I hadn't noticed earlier and we were cutting across the grass between the thin castle and the woods concealing the church, with the statue of the boy shrinking behind my right shoulder. The grass was rougher here and littered with pieces of fallen wood. The jeep buried them, or smashed them or hurled them aside. We glimpsed another building in the trees to our left. It was like a long cylinder upended and it was orange and tall and topped with a naked male figure whose head was as high as the top branches of the beech trees. We were travelling due south now, racing the sun, and then we hit another road and turned right on to it. We were back in the trees where I had been the night before, in the wood in front of the churchyard – but the other end of it.

The trees began to get closer, the vegetation thicker, and then we ran out of road. The Kid skidded to a halt again. He grabbed a bag from the passenger well and jumped out. I climbed out, too, and followed him in the direction of the church, waiting for the shove from behind and the sound of rasping breath and tortured lungs. But neither came. I turned round. The Killer had vanished.

The Kid opened the door of the church and we walked in. The ceiling was surprisingly high, supported by a ribcage of dark beams. Opposite the door there was a slab of marble with a haloed saint in pinks and mauves. At the far end by the altar were two girls, side by side, with their backs to us. They were wearing white dresses. They had white lilies in their hair. The Kid had opened the bag. He shoved a grey jacket at me. He put on one the same. When we had looked at each other and straightened each other's lapels and darts, we marched up the aisle, red carnations in our buttonholes. We stopped behind the girls and looked over their shoulders as they reached out in front of them and took tiny wafers from a silver plate. They ate the wafers and then one reached for a glass of wine the same colour as our carnations, which she sipped, before handing it on to the other. Behind us the organ started to play the 'Wedding March'. I turned round and saw the Killer leaning on the rail of the organ loft, watching us, holding the mask to his face. The girls turned round to face us – they were the two actresses from the Hall. Their hair was tied identically, their faces were made up the same. Catherine stared at me, her face empty. The Kid moved to one side, so I did, too, and then the girls began walking back down the aisle and we followed them.

We went outside again and a snowstorm of confetti swirled around us. I looked up at the wall of the church but I couldn't see where it had come from or who had thrown it. The Kid reached for his girl and she gave him her cheek and he kissed it. The bells had started to ring. I looked at Catherine. She had turned her cheek, too. I kissed her. The Kid and his girl and Catherine and I held hands and walked back to the jeep. When we got there, the Killer was already in his seat. The dummies were in a heap in the undergrowth, their limbs buckled and twisted. The Kid's girl sat on the Killer's lap and held his mask on for him. Catherine and I were in the back. The Kid turned the jeep round and headed back the way we had come. The Killer pulled his girl's hand aside and let out a 'Yee-hah'. Then she clamped his face again. Both Catherine and the other girl were looking to the left, their faces turned away from me and the Kid. The Killer was bouncing up and down in his seat, exaggerating the movement of the jeep across the road. His girl's legs were slightly apart. She held his hand between them.

The Kid drove slower this time and when we were out of the woods he turned right instead of left. Soon we were travelling behind the lake, moving smoothly on a well-made road. We could see over to the south lawn and up to the Hall, spread across the top of the gradient. Although we were a couple of hundred yards away from it, it still dominated the view. Alone and massive, long and low, with calm water and level grass in front of it and blue sky behind. Elegant and arrogant.

The jeep gradually came to a halt and the Kid pulled off the road. We got out and I followed him, with the others behind us, down to the water's edge. The Kid and I stopped there but the Killer had the two girls by their hands. The three of them walked into the water. The Killer stood his ground in the shallows but the two girls joined hands and carried on. Twenty yards or so further out in the lake there was a figure facing us. He was tall and green above the water and he stood holding a trident. He beckoned with his other hand towards the girls. They turned and looked back towards me and the Kid. The Kid shook his head. The girls carried on. As they got closer to Neptune and sank lower in the water, their dresses billowed up behind them. Before they got to him, they were already out of their depth and the water had closed over their heads. I turned to look at the Kid. His arm was levelled at Neptune and his hand held a gun. Neptune stared back at the Kid. The Kid fired three times. Neptune slipped down into the water. But he did it in his own time. He wasn't hurt. Then he, too, vanished. I carried on staring across the lake and so did the Kid, who had let his arm drop to his side, but there was no sign of any of them. There were rushes around us and they followed the curve of the lake. The girls could have made it there, underwater, if they were strong swimmers. Either that or they really had gone to meet Neptune. The Killer grabbed me by the arm again. This time I shook him off. I was worried about the girls. When he grabbed my arm once more, he almost pulled it from its socket.

'Where are they?' I asked. That was when he smacked me across the face with the back of his hand.

Back in the jeep, we were flying again, now that the girls were gone. The Kid was going faster than ever and the Killer was urging him on, pumping his spare hand through the air. We had left the lake behind us. Soon I saw the orange cylinder-shaped tower pass by again, but this time on our left as we travelled behind it. Maybe the figure on top could see the Hall from up there. We began to move uphill, and then we saw what looked like a wooden stockade appear ahead of us – like something out of an old western. The Kid slammed the jeep into the dust outside a tall wooden door, topped with stakes, with 'Tombstone' stencilled across it in a 'Wanted' poster script. We all got out. The Killer pushed open the door.

Inside was a western town. There was a jail, a sheriff's office and a saloon. In front of the saloon there were horse-rails and troughs. There was a hotel called the Columbia – that was the name of the place where the Britpop 'in' crowd used to hang out. Behind it, on the other side of the compound, a wooden watchtower stood on stilts. The ground was all dust and dirt. The 'Sheriff' sign creaked in the wind. All the doors were shut. There were no people, no horses and no dogs. There were no tumbling chords from a bar-room piano spilling out through the saloon doors.

The Kid looked at the Killer, who was scanning the set. The Kid seemed to be asking for instructions, or some kind of guidance. The Killer took the mask away from his face, stuck his nose in the air and sniffed the breeze.

'Women,' he said, his voice rasping, too, and then he put the mask back on. Sure enough, on the balcony of the Columbia Hotel, a woman appeared – a western bad girl in a red dress, trimmed with black. She leaned against the rail, put her foot up on the fencing and drew on a cigarette. A scarlet ribbon trailed from her hair. Then, next to her, a man in a cowboy hat appeared. He was carrying a TV set. He heaved it on to the rail and then launched it into space. It plummeted but then thudded dully, disappointingly, on to the ground, its insides spilling only slightly on to the dirt. A muted cheer came from inside the hotel and I heard someone shout, 'Ride her, cowboy', and then the music started up – 'Cigarettes and Alcohol' by Oasis. The woman walked down the staircase, swinging her hips and tossing her head, and began to head for the saloon. The Killer followed her and the Kid and I were right behind. We pushed open the doors and walked on to the sawdust.

Inside there was a barman polishing glasses – 'James' from the scene in the drawing room – and a table where the man who had played Paul was sitting. The woman – it was Mary, the maid – sat down opposite him. The rest of the place was deserted. We walked up to the bar and the Kid ordered whiskies all round. The man at the table was drunk. He began ranting away at Mary. She had a black eye and sat with her arms and legs crossed, staring at the wall.

'You've had your way with just about every cocksucker in town,' he said, waving his arm round the empty room.

The Kid didn't look interested, he had downed his whisky and was walking towards the saloon door again – but the Killer was listening. Then the man at the table called Mary a 'pox-ridden whore'. She uncrossed her arms – and spat at him. The man stood up and tried to hit her but suddenly the Killer was next to him, mask still clamped to his face. He held the other man's arm in mid-air, before wrenching it down to his side. Through his mask the Killer said:

'I screwed your wife.'

His voice sounded metallic and fuzzy, robotic.

The other guy just stared at him. Mary stood up, though – and now she spat at the Killer. He looked at her, wiped the spit from his face and moved the mask enough to slip it into his mouth. Then the woman laughed, and then she laughed at her husband. Then she grabbed the Killer's hand and left the bar with him, swishing her skirts all the way. The Kid, who was standing by the swing doors, moved aside to let them through. The Killer barked something to him through the mask as he left.

The Kid beckoned to me. I walked towards him. By the time I got to the saloon doors he was already halfway to the Columbia Hotel. The Killer and Mary had disappeared. There was a wooden staircase leading up the side of the hotel to the balcony. I followed the Kid up. The music grew louder as we climbed. There was shouting and laughing, too, and then the sound of glass and wood shattering and splintering. As I got to the top of the stairs the door to the room where all the action was going on slammed shut. As I passed it there was a loud thud as something – or someone – hit it from the other side. I carried on behind the Kid who was turning into a room further along.

It was nearly dark in there. There was a curtain almost closed across the window at the far end, blowing in the breeze and flicking tiny patches of light on to the wall. In the corner by the window there was a girl in white petticoats, with her feet drawn up, sitting on a chair. The Kid was standing in front of her and she was holding the white lace tight against her shins and staring at his feet. Although it was gloomy in there and the girl's head was down I was sure that it was Catherine. On the wall, next to a tiny crucifix, there was a photograph of a young girl smiling on a high-wire at the top of a circus tent.

The Kid had obviously said something to Catherine, but I had arrived too late to hear it. He was waiting for a reply but she was saying nothing. He flicked a coin in the air, caught it and put it back in his pocket without looking at it. Then he moved across to a tatty dresser that was leaning at an angle against the wall and swept his hand across the top, sending everything that was on it flying – bottles of perfume, a framed photo of a man, a hip flask, some cheap jewellery. And then he pulled open the drawers and started ransacking them, hurling their contents on to the floor. Catherine didn't move. Then the Kid triumphantly plucked out a roll of banknotes tied with a stocking. He stuffed the money into a pocket and turned back to Catherine.

'You've been sussed,' he said. 'You should have been more careful. Anyone in this town gets hold of that sort of money they keep their mouth shut. Didn't you know about me? Didn't you hear about me? Didn't they tell you I was in town? You've got half an hour to grab everything you own and get out of here. If you're here when I come back I'll break your fingers.'

He clapped his hands. 'Stand up.'

Catherine lifted her head to look at him but stayed where she was.

The Kid darted towards her and grabbed her arm.

'I said, "Stand up".'

He wrenched her to her feet.

'Up against the wall.'

She moved slowly to her left and stood there silently.

'Put out your arms.'

She moved them from her sides.

'Straight out.'

Her arms were spread now, horizontally against the wall.

'Victim,' the Kid spat and turned towards the door.

I looked at Catherine. She gave me a sly look. I left her and went with the Kid.

I looked down from the top of the staircase. I could see over the palisade, out on to the tops of the trees. I could see bits of the Hall behind them – it was like a giant creature asleep on the ground, hidden in undergrowth. The Kid skipped the last three steps and began heading back across the sandy ground. He kicked up tiny clouds of dry dirt, whistling tunelessly as he went. I followed him. He stopped outside the Sheriff's office. The window was open. He was looking inside and listening.

I looked through the window, too. Behind the sheriff's desk there was a woman in a grey suit. In front of it a man lounged, collar undone, feet up on a stool, a cigarette dangling from a hand.

'Please, Charles,' the woman said. It was the other actress from the Hall – the one who looked as though she could have been Catherine's sister.

The man smirked. It was 'Paul' again, with his hair slicked back and a new moustache.

'I'd like to help you, Edith,' he said, 'but you're in a no-win situation. It wouldn't do either of us any good. The major's nervous. He needs you to carry the can. You're the fall girl. There are too many bodies, Edie, you know that. You can't explain them away any more. Last plane in at the airport, there was a conveyor belt for them. We can screw again later, if you like. I can help you that much.'

Edith looked distracted. Her hands were clasped together on the desk.

'I need your support, Chuck,' she said. 'If I know you're with me I can be strong. I can see this through. I can come out the other side. You're part of my life. You're all over my house. Your things… Your clothes. I can smell you as soon as I walk in my front door, Chuck. I go into my bedroom and I smell you on my sheets. '

'Edie,' he said. 'Sweetheart. You know what I need, I've never made any secret of it. But you know what I can't stand, too. And you know what I can't give you. Look on the bright side. What you've done won't go unnoticed. I'll make sure they know. Even if I have to whisper it.'

Edith leant back in her seat and Chuck got to his feet. He came up to us at the window and looked out at the deserted set of Tombstone, with the muted carousing from the Columbia the only evidence of life.

Then he opened the door and came out past us, heading for the hotel. We watched him cross the square and climb the stairs and then the sounds from behind the door grew louder for a second as it opened, and then dropped again once he was inside.

We turned back to the window to find that a new figure had taken Chuck's place in front of Edith at the desk. It was the newest of the male actors, the one who looks like Haines, the one who had been in the pilot's seat of the light aircraft. He was dressed as he had been then, in the same helmet and suit, but he had a kind of unearthly glow about him now. They must have done something to his clothes – and his face. Edith was staring fixedly at him.

'Listen to me, Edith,' he said. 'Don't do it for the major. He's yesterday's man. He's not worth it. But watch your back – he can still hurt you. And forget about Chuck, let him go screw himself. Don't worry, though, you're being looked after. The angels are getting their wings dirty for you.' He put his hand on her shoulder. 'You're scared, aren't you? Of standing up, high above the crowds and shouting it out? I know what it's like – to be up in the sky, looking down, believing you're going to die. Confront your demons, Edith. Get up there, look them in the eyes and dare them to cast you down. Don't be afraid of death. But beware of the dead. You can't seduce them. You can't change them. They're up high. They can see it all from up there, Edith.'

The flyer got to his feet and walked over to the window.

Inches from us, he began to speak again.

'Hey, guess what? They say there's gold out there in the hills. Well, I never found it.'

He looked across the town. His eyes rose to the hotel.

'We're gonna raze that place to the ground, Edie. For Andreas. For Gudrun. For Ulrike.'

The flyer stared grimly at the Columbia for a moment and then he turned and walked out of the door, heading for the saloon. The Kid walked into the sheriff's office through the open door and I went in after him. Edith had got up. She was pulling at a metal ring embedded in the floor. She heaved up a trap door and stood holding it open. I could see the top of a wooden staircase. The Kid made for the hole and began climbing down. I followed him.

Down there it was like a basement flat. In the ceiling at the far end, below Edith's desk, was a set of three lights, at different angles, bleaching everything immediately below them but casting triangular shadows on to our end of the room. Under the lights were a double mattress, a couple of blankets and a few cushions. On the mattress lay two men – one, arms behind his head, staring at the ceiling, the other sitting up and slamming a baseball from one hand to the other. On the floor between us and them were several empty tins of food and cans of beer, some scattered newspapers, a couple of open packets of biscuits and an old typewriter.

The man with the baseball was the actor who had just played Chuck. Although his hair was the same, the moustache had gone and he was wearing dark glasses. He stopped throwing the ball and instead pushed aside the blanket and got to his feet. He was naked. He began pulling on a pair of jeans. The actor who had played the barman pulled the blanket back over himself and continued to stare at the ceiling.

'I'm going mad in here, Ed,' he said. 'I've had it. I'm going downtown. I'll get us some beers.'

'If you move from this room,' Ed said, 'I'll put a bullet between your eyes.'

He put his hands on his hips.

'Five minutes,' the other man whined, 'that's all I want. I just want to see the sky, feel the concrete under my feet. If you don't let me out I'm gonna go crazy.'

'You know the score, Jim. We stay here another two days. If you can't handle that I'll sort it out for you. I'll pump you full of Nocturne and you can spend the time unconscious. It's no skin off my nose. If you never wake up again, it's no problem. I'll do this on my own if I have to.'

'You'd better watch your back,' said Jim petulantly. 'I ain't afraid to use a gun either, you know.'

Ed snorted and began rolling a cigarette.

'Chuck would have let me go,' Jim tried again.

'Big Daddy's not going to ride to your rescue this time, little boy, you'd better get used to that,' said Ed, measuring his words. 'Chuck pissed us around once too often. There's mixing it and there's betrayal. Chuck got himself a little too comfortable in bed with the enemy. He liked it there. It was nice and warm. You'd better watch you don't follow him, boy.'

'I'm with you, Ed,' simpered Jim. 'I'm loyal, you know that.' He put his head on one side. 'All I want is five minutes, Ed.'

'We stick to the plan,' said the other man. 'We don't budge from here till Wednesday. Wednesday we move. Wednesday you get to use your gun. If you're a good boy. And then, when it's done, we come back here.' He jerked his thumb up behind him towards the hotel. 'And we blow that place to kingdom come.'

The lights went out. The Kid pushed past me and led the way back up the steps.

Back outside the sheriff's office we could see movement on the balcony of the Columbia Hotel. It was the Killer. With one hand he was zipping up his flies while with the other he clutched his mask. As he started down the stairs, the Kid began heading out of the compound. I was close behind. The Kid swung open the gate. A cowboy on horseback came galloping through. He whooped as he passed us and then came to a halt in a burst of sand and stones. It was the actor who looked like Haines, his face still shining. We watched him as he tied up his horse and made for the saloon. When he pushed open the swing doors we heard a loud cheer and then a drinking song started up inside, accompanied by shouts and the sound of glasses clunking against one another. The Killer had ignored all of us as he walked back across the stockade. He was already sitting in the jeep when we turned round. We went to join him. For a second I caught a glimpse of reflected light up at the top of the watchtower, and then we were away again, the Kid at the wheel, heading back towards the Hall.

The Kid stopped outside, motor running, while I got out. I was only just clear of the jeep when he stamped down on the accelerator and took off back towards the arch. I turned round and walked back up to the entrance. I hauled myself up the steps. Inside the North Hall, I closed the door behind me and stood there, leaning on it. Inside it was cool and peaceful and still. All that flat, solid stone around me. Under my feet and high above my head. Radiating out from my body.

My arm was twitching as I lay on my bed. I lay there watching the skin below my elbow jump as if there was another, miniature heart under the surface.

Stevenson was serving me again at supper. I hadn't expected that. He was polite, too, as if something had somehow cleared the air between us. I don't know what that could have been as I haven't seen him all day. Well, whatever it was, I was happy if it was going to put a civil tongue back inside his head. He even smiled as he handed me my food and was kind enough to ask how things had gone today.

'Well, it could have been better,' I replied. 'But perhaps you could say that I learnt something.'

'Well, if we can learn a little something each day, sir, then we can at least be sure that we are constantly making progress in our continual quest for enlightenment.'

'How many staff do you have here, Stevenson?' I asked.

'Well, sir, you know Mary and Henri and then there is Matthew, the odd-job man.'

'You manage all this between the four of you?'

'Under my direction, sir, my team work hard and efficiently. And Mr Haines's household is a small one. There is of course the outside team. Donald, the head gardener, with his own crew of three older gentlemen with whom he administers the grounds. Old Lionel is quite a sight seated on his mower!'

'And Catherine – does she get involved in the running of the house at all?'

'My lady is gracious enough to leave that side of things to me, sir. And now, if you will excuse me, I have various things to attend to.'

'Of course – oh, any luck with the internet connection?'

A puzzled expression came over Stevenson's face.

'I'm afraid that still has us rather vexed, sir. Rest assured that we are doing everything we can.'

I've been lying here, trying to sleep. Drunken singing and shouting outside, the sound of breaking glass. I think I heard Haines's voice out there. It must be the actors. They've just started singing 'No one likes us, we don't care...' They were right underneath my window for a while. I looked out but I couldn't see much, just dark shapes shifting across the grass, arms lifted, legs sagging. It's cloudy tonight, no moon or stars.

They've wandered off now. I'll be able to sleep.

Editor's note—

And so we leave the writer trying to sleep. And return to this morning – when he was failing to wake.

Pity poor Mary attempting to rouse him from his dark dreams! The sleep of the ignorant and obtuse has a gluey stodginess that will respond only to something a sight more brutal than her soft entreaties.

Ah, good old Stevenson, come to blast the glue asunder! Yes, writer, he was busy yesterday. There is more to his life than dealing with yours, you know. Stevenson must take his duties seriously and he must also practise his tricks.

The writer casts his gaze towards the jeep – there is no sign of Stevenson, he reports. What use has he made of the third eye? Were we given the pineal gland for nothing?

The back seat of the jeep. Only a dummy would fail to recognise a dummy.

The dummies' dead victim eyes are wide open inside their masks. In *Seance on a Wet Afternoon* we see reflections of trees in the goggles of Billy the abductor, obscuring his eyes, as he stashes his motorcycle in preparation for the kidnap. The abduction itself was filmed in Weybridge – next door to Mr Haines's home town of Walton on Thames.

The 'Killer' and the 'Kid'. Very well. The terminology has meaning. The administration – or self-administration – of drugs and the varying combinations of need, desire, courage and cowardice involved, can often be an interesting topic of conversation. But is the Killer a killer? Or just a bald-headed pussy cat with an interest in amateur theatricals? The blow that he later aims at the writer may give us pause for thought.

The Kid, as a matter of interest, is the son of the older of the male actors. A child star in a showbiz family.

The treatment meted out to the writer inside the warehouse is valid. If a man fails to respond appropriately to a single light aircraft on fire then he must be confronted with a second. It is hard not to see this episode as a very personal warning to the writer. The violence of the attack on him, combined with the intense depiction of mental imbalance with which he is presented, create a message about what is to come that he will ignore at his peril.

The wedding scene is touching (Catherine, an amateur, shows all the calm steeliness of the professional with that kiss). The men seem so powerless, do they not, in the face of the exercise of the female prerogative – in this case to seek a watery death?

Talking of weddings reminds me of one that never was. It should have taken place in this very church. The bride-never-to-be was Estelle, only daughter of the second Earl, and her beau was the Reverend Christopher Crofton, a young vicar who had recently been granted his own parish a few miles from the Hall. The two were very much in love. Although the Reverend Crofton had a settled life ahead of him and would certainly have been able to provide adequately for Estelle, this would not have been sufficient for her to continue to live in the style to which she had been accustomed. The Earl, despite the tears of his daughter – who cared not a jot about this –and the wholesome entreaties of his would-be son-in-law, forbade the marriage. The couple tried everything they could to get him to change his mind, but in vain. Finally, they took the desperate step of attempting to tie the knot without his blessing in a village church in Hampshire. Unfortunately the vicar was an acquaintance of the Earl and, after inviting the couple to come back to the church the next day to be united in holy matrimony, he sent a message to the Hall enquiring whether the young lady's father was aware of their intentions. The next morning, the Earl was driven to the village and when, shortly after his arrival, his daughter and her intended returned to the church, they found him standing in the arched doorway, blocking their path. At this, despite her lover's impassioned assertions that he would never give her up, poor Estelle became convinced that their union was never meant to be. She returned home with her father, to whom she did not speak during the whole journey.

A week later she was on her way to a sanatorium in Malvern, where she took a vow of silence and spent the thirty years until her father's death knitting blankets for the poor. The day after he went to meet his maker, she left the sanatorium, walked into an inn in the town and ordered herself a roast dinner, which she proceeded to eat, washed down with a glass of port, quite alone – to the shock of both the staff and the inn's customers. Returning the next day to the Hall she had not seen for half a lifetime, she arranged with her brother, now the third Earl, to have the small income he agreed to provide her with from his own inheritance invested in a new charitable foundation that she would run, for the benefit of impoverished clergymen wishing to marry and provide comfortably for their wives. She also joined with her mother in the post-funeral arrangements for the second Earl – of which more anon. (She was the one firing the shotgun in the air in order to cause the pigs to stampede, and screaming in delight when they began to attack the mound of earth).

Tombstone. Quick-change girls – hair blow-dried, still a bit damp, looking like sweat. More victims. Some more willing than others. Violence interceding with violence. Just like a real western. And the thieves become terrorists. And the uber-thief ascends to the political sphere. And the strange pilot – Mr Haines informs me, incidentally, that by the time of this album he 'had a morbid fear of flying and would only travel by car or train' – returns on horseback to drink in the saloon. There is a song on *After Murder Park* called 'Dead Sea Navigators'. It was a chorus in the Navigators' honour that was heard in the saloon at the end of this scene. They are hardened drinkers, life wasters, doomed to wander fitfully in the shadow of death before the final last orders.

Aha! The writer sees a reflected light at the top of the watchtower! He has finally noticed something! What a shame that he fails to follow it up. Who knows what else he might have discovered?

Maybe we should feel a touch of sympathy for the writer when he takes comfort from the stone of the North Hall – bearing in mind the aural history buried inside it. Think of the crack of muskets, the clash of swords, the shouts and the screams as monarchy and democracy, father and son, past and future vied for supremacy in this vaulted chamber.

We have already noted the second Earl's enjoyment of the instruments of war – and of the way he managed to combine it with a contempt for animal life. There are other examples. Holidaying once in France on the country estate of some Duc or other, his host kindly deposited a hundred of his home-bred pheasants in a large netted enclosure that had been especially erected on one of his fields. The two nobles, together with a handful of other invited guests, then blazed away manfully with their shotguns until the birds were all slaughtered and either lay on the ground, awash in their own blood, or hung entangled in the tented web of their death chamber. A tally was taken and the Earl was adjudged to have murdered the second highest total – behind only the teenage daughter of the Duc.

Today's performance in front of the writer was based on the third Auteurs album *After Murder Park*. The front cover of this features a distorted black and white shot of the wood in said park. It is like a still from a cheap horror film. The camera looks as though it has cut away from the blood-spilling, perhaps following the victim's eyes up to the trees. It is reminiscent of a shot in *Seance on a Wet Afternoon*. Here, Billy is about to appear in a wood where he is to bury the child he is supposed to have killed. We see the trees sideways on, as if from the perspective of someone lying on the ground. Then the view turns through ninety degrees and we see them upright. Billy appears through the mist, the girl in his arms, wrapped in a blanket. The branches of the trees on the album sleeve look like arms with claws. The 'Murder' in the title is written in red, as if in the victim's blood. Inside the CD case, there is a photo of a group of children with distorted faces. Children as adults in immature bodies, children with Mr Haines's grown-up face. Lots of little Mr Haineses.

Two of the most significant songs were missing from the performance of *After Murder Park* – 'Unsolved Child Murder' and the title track. But do not worry. They will be along later.

The writer welcomes the return of a 'civil tongue' to Stevenson's head. Should he have chosen his words more carefully, even while believing that they would pass no further? But once a writer's words have passed from his head they have already escaped from his control. He cannot know where they will end up. There is a worrying change of tone evident every now and then in the writer's attitude to Stevenson. He should watch his step there.

Stevenson leans over the writer as he serves him. He needs to be careful. And I hope he is shaving assiduously. A little stubble in the wrong place could prove his downfall.

The servants – what a motley crew. A failure of capitalisation will prove the downfall of any organisation.

'Mr Haines possibly among those serenading the Dead Sea Navigators on the lawns of the Hall? Well, what would be the point of creating an ideal drinking crew if one could not join in the fun? I believe they kicked off with the song from the saloon – 'Streets of Laredo', an old cowboy lament for a dead comrade. In Mr Haines's own song the Navigators have passed on. The old crew has shrunk. But the remaining drinking companions soldier on. Tonight was a pissed-up, football-song-chanting commemoration of the ignoble dead.

The English have a natural taste for disorder, Mr Paxman says in his book *The English: A Portrait of a People*. It exists alongside their desire for tolerance and fairplay. Local fighting became common in the 1500s, he informs us, but there was always a ritualistic element to it and a sense that there must always be limits. Let us hope that still applies.

After Murder Park. The title sends a chill down one's spine, does it not? This record is a masterpiece of perverted politics, war, misanthropy and murder, written while Mr Haines was observing life from his wheelchair – at the level of belly, groin and curled fist. The disc was produced by Mr Steve Albini, the man who had defined the sound of grunge in the States. Trust Mr Haines to take him on when grunge was finally over – when Britpop, his mutant child, had replaced it. Mr Haines is a man defiantly out of time! At the start of 1995, when he was starting to write the record, the cursèd Britpop was everywhere. While outside Britain was reliving the sunny, optimistic sixties, Mr Haines was confined in the gloom writing about murder and hate. But what better filter through which to view the flaccid rise of the Britpop pretenders, so baggy in Mr Haines's discarded trousers?

In March Blur were given four Brit awards – and then Damon Albarn met Tony Blair to discuss an 'accord'. Unfortunately this was never to become a reality, but what a glorious achievement it would have been – the union of Britpop and Brit pop-politics. Britain would surely have entered the kind of golden age that would have put the Ancient Greeks to shame. Yes, everyone wanted a slice of Britpop pie, but the man who had invented the recipe was being ignored. Not to worry though – the evil genius was in his secret hideaway, planning his revenge.

It was a dry, warm summer that year. The pop kids danced without a care. Rubbish blew along the streets, chased by salivating dogs. Blur played in front of thousands at the Mile End Stadium. Pulp wooed the Common People. At Abbey Road Studios, where the Auteurs were recording *After Murder Park*, Paul McCartney popped in for tea.

In mid-August came 'Blur vs Oasis' week. Who would be No.1? Who gave a shit? Not Mr Haines, that is for sure. On the 16th a television programme called *Britpop Now* was broadcast, featuring all the 'hot' new bands in the 'new scene'. How many Auteurs songs would there be, how much coverage would there be for the man who started it all? Not one. None.

It was winter before anything from the Abbey Road sessions seeped out on to the now cold, wet streets. In November white labels of 'Meet Me at the Airport', a *Baader Meinhof* song recorded during spare time there, were reviewed. Press copies were accompanied by a page from the *Anarchist Cookbook* on how to build a nail bomb. Mr Haines reviewed the single himself early in the new year when he was assessing the week's releases for *Select* magazine. After all, what did he know about this strange new band called 'Baader Meinhof'? He gave it a rave. The same week, the Auteurs released 'Back With the Killer Again' – those delightful corpses in anti-contamination suits on the front of the sleeve, 'Good Cop Bad Cop' spray-painted on the wall behind them. The cops in question were the two head honchos from Hut Records, Mr Haines's record company. Yes, the Killer got them both.

Mr Haines's good friends from Creation Records had moved in down the road now. Handy for when he ran out of sugar.

Mr Haines was most forthcoming when I grilled him about *After Murder Park* during our little chat. But then one can afford to be indulgent when one has created a work of such brilliance.

By this point in our conversation the great man's gaze had

turned to the row of his own CDs that takes pride of place on his shelves. A rather dreamy, replete expression filled his face.

'Did you approach the album with the idea of writing a group of songs that had a kind of unity,' I asked, 'or did that idea develop as you wrote it?'

Reluctantly he dragged his gaze from his canon and faced me once more.

'I wanted the whole album to be like a loose narrative movie,' he replied. 'Me as writer/director, Albini as cameraman and Abbey Road Studio 2 as the set.'

What a delightful picture – Hollywood recreated and replaced in England.

'If you hadn't been so lamentably confined to a wheelchair when you wrote it,' I said, 'and I congratulate you, sir, on your fortitude during that period, how different do you think it would have been?'

He nodded graciously at me.

'I think the accident just intensified the approach,' he responded. 'I had already written 'Light Aircraft', 'Land Lovers', 'New Brat', 'Everything You Say', so I had made inroads. Also Albini was on board long before the accident.'

'Was writing and recording the album a cathartic experience?'

'Recording it certainly was – mainly due to Albini. His opinion was that good will out. He absolutely took no shit from anyone in the music business. It was good to be recording that album as so called Britpop took off.' Mr Haines was rolling his 'r's now. 'I had until that point met no one who truly viewed the music business the way I did. Steve and I were for a while an allied force.'

'Was there anything in particular that informed the songs of *After Murder Park*?'

'The 1964 Bryan Forbes film *Seance on a Wet Afternoon* was a big influence. The entrapment of the couple in the film seemed to echo a lot of what I was going through at the time. The album is really about claustrophobia, and how ordinary people overcome – or do not – all that is thrown at them.'

'I suppose that is the main concern of 'Unsolved Child Murder'?'

Mr Haines paused for a moment before he answered. When he did it was in a very matter-of-fact tone.

'When I was five,' he said, 'the kid at the end of the road disappeared and was found dead – murdered.' He looked across the room to the far wall. 'His father was a doctor.'

'What impact did this incident have on you?'

Mr Haines's gaze returned to me.

'Up until that point, I had believed – naively – that the healing powers of doctors made them and their families untouchable by tragedy.'

And now his eyes narrowed in contemplation. For a few moments each of us sat with our thoughts. Each listening to the sound of one hand clapping.

Day Five

I made it down for breakfast on time today. I didn't want Stevenson bursting in again. The actors were down the far end of the dining room when I got there, but they had nearly finished eating. They were all dressed casually: T-shirts, jeans and trainers – I'd half-expected army fatigues and machine gun belts. When they were all ready they filed out together. Catherine was the last. She turned and gave me a faint smile.

It was a beautiful day outside. I took my glass of fresh orange juice and walked up to the window. The trees, pinned back by all that closely-mown grass, were shimmering. The grass strong and moist. Sunlight was shining on the surface of the lake. You could imagine the Earls standing here, one by one, over the years, looking out at all that was theirs, and each repeating 'God's in His heaven – All's right with the world!' It was a bit different for me, though. I didn't own any of this, I was here under sufferance. I couldn't control anything that happened here.

I was surprised when Stevenson came up to me then and started chatting about the view. He told me about the Viscount's Arch. It used to be a residential building, he said, but no one lived there any more. It had always been occupied by the estate's gamekeeper but apparently the last man to hold down the job, in the days of the third Earl, had blown his brains out in there. Something about unrequited love for the lady of the house.

I was even more surprised when Stevenson asked me if I would 'care to be outside, on the steps, any time between nine thirty and ten' – whatever suited me. Then he and I would take a ride out to the wrecked car, where the day's 'entertainment' would begin. That it would be him going with me and not the Killer and the Kid was a good sign. But maybe Stevenson would only take me as far as the car? Maybe they would be waiting there, the one pulling on his toxic gas, the other dragging on a cigarette, ready to take me on another hellish merry-go-round ride?

At nine forty-five I stood on the north steps of the house, looking across the fields to a tightly drawn-down sky.

From the left, a crimson Daimler approached. It had come from the direction of the power yard. I can hear the hum of the generator in that place from my room. At night I sometimes lie awake listening to it. And then, slowly, it lulls me to sleep. It has a gentle pitch. It winds down at intervals, the revolutions of its engine gradually decreasing. It's warm, regular and mechanical.

The car pulled up in front of me. I walked down the last few steps and then round its silver-grilled shark-head hood. Stevenson had pushed open the passenger door for me and I climbed into the leather seat. The dashboard was wooden and curved, and inset with so many glass-fronted dials that it looked like the control panel of an airliner. I could smell Stevenson's aftershave, but there was another fragrance, too, fainter, that I couldn't place. I turned round. The back seat was empty, but there was a bowler hat on the rear shelf.

Stevenson said, 'Are you comfortable, sir?', and then eased us away in the direction of the arch.

'It's a beautiful car, Stevenson,' I said.

'It used to belong to my father, sir. It was a present to him from his old employer. For many years' loyal service. My father – bless him – could never bring himself actually to use it, though. He believed himself to be unworthy. He polished it every weekend and sat in it, and then replaced it in his garage. As you can see, sir, I have no such qualms.'

As we had back on the first day, we pulled up short of the

wrecked car and continued on foot. We walked towards it and everything seemed to be the same – the mannequin was lying as we had left her. As we came closer, though, it became obvious that in fact something had changed. It was no longer a mannequin, it was a young woman, lying in the same attitude, with the same senseless expression. She was wearing the same clothes, ripped and stained in the same places.

We stood opposite the wreck, looking at it from the other side of the road. Then Stevenson crossed over and I followed him. Standing a few feet away from the woman, it was obvious that, despite her dishevelled hair, closed eyes and charred, cut face, she was the second actress – although for a moment I had thought it might be Catherine. I looked at the car behind her. Slumped against steering wheel and dashboard, horribly mangled, were two mannequins like the ones I had travelled with in the jeep, but both dressed in black polo-neck jumpers.

And then the actress's eyes opened. She stared at the ground blankly for a moment, as if trying to remember why she was there, before lifting her head and looking me in the eyes. Then she raised herself into a sitting position. Slipping backwards into the car, she sat on the edge of the driver's seat and pulled out a handbag. Holding a hand-mirror to her face, she began to paw at the blood, dirt and oil with a wet tissue. Then she took out a brush and worked on her hair. There wasn't much she could do with the tears and stains to her clothes, but she made the few minor readjustments that were possible. Then she looked straight at me and began to speak.

'I always knew this was how I would die,' she said. 'My whole life flashed in front of me as we crashed. It's true – it really happens. First I was playing in the garden in a never-ending summer. Then running round the school playground. Then playing party games. And dancing at discos. Boys and booze. Christmases and New Year's Eves. Coming of age – Mummy's and Daddy's friends. Old men and women. Drunken speeches. Drunken uncles. Crappy presents – because I already had everything. Apart from the things that money can't buy – even when Daddy's a millionaire.' She had taken a lipstick from her bag now and was applying it in the mirror, freeze-framing an air-kiss to herself. 'A week later they came for me – no masks, no guns, no shouting. They took me when I was shopping. Liberated me from the bags full of clothes. Bundled me into a car. They were my age, dressed like my friends, smiling and laughing. I thought it was a practical joke. In the back seat, a hand and a cloth. The smell of chloroform. Out for the count.

'When I woke up, out on the farm, in the middle of nowhere, I was excited! Gagged and giggling. I was glad to have been taken away, glad not to have to go back.' She laughed. 'It was really living, being out there with them. Miles from anywhere but out in the world. I'd never lived like that before. And I'd never lived with danger. With the possibility that soon I might die. When they told me how much they wanted for me I laughed. I said, "Ask for twice as much." Daddy was worth so much more.' She took a packet of cigarettes from her bag and, crossing her legs, lit one. She held the packet out to me but I shook my head. 'We talked about politics. Or rather they talked and I listened. They were well-informed and passionate. They convinced me. They deserve Daddy's money so much more than he does. We were going to take it and leave the country. Go somewhere we could use it. Oh well. I still miss home, you know. Even though I hate it. Because it's in my blood. Will you phone my parents, let them know what's happened? Tell them, "We've found your daughter"?' She trembled slightly. 'My mother's so fragile. Weak and defenceless. She's just a child. Do you know what that was like for me?' Her voice grew fainter. 'To have a child for a mother?'

With that, her head sank on to her chest. Stevenson reached forward, took the cigarette from her fingers and ground it into the dirt.

'Come on, sir,' he said, gently pulling on my arm. 'There's nothing we can do for her now.'

As I stood up, he reached into the car and picked her up. Then he spread her out on the ground, her arms draped extravagantly about her head, eyes wide open, fixed on the sky.

We headed east, past the castle, and soon we were in the

woods again. This time the trees were lower. Sunlight flickered through gaps in the branches and bits of blue sky fluttered like turquoise tinsel. Then suddenly we were out and back in the open. The sky flung up above us like a huge flag. Then we turned off the road, through an open gate and into a rough, stony field. The car coped easily – it's like being inside a giant mechanical arm with steel muscles. The other side of the field was another gate – closed. We stopped in front of it.

'Would you be so kind, sir?' Stevenson asked.

I climbed out, unfastened it and stood while Stevenson drove the car through.

I rejoined the car on a concrete track the other side of the narrow lane we had just crossed.

'Are we still on the estate?' I asked as we drove on.

'Indeed we are, sir,' Stevenson replied. 'You would know if you were leaving it. You will find that all the entry and exit points to Mr Haines's property are securely sealed. It was something he worked very hard on as soon as he took up residence here. The area we have just entered, however, is one that is not covered by the strict planning laws regarding building and refurbishment that apply to the rest of his land. As will be evident shortly.' He lowered his voice. 'What we are about to see is a building quite out of keeping with anything else you will have seen on your stay.'

The concrete track curved round to the left and when it straightened again it turned into a short section of tarmacked road, with a neat pavement on one side. Leading from the pavement to our left were two small driveways, separated by elm trees in pebbled circles in the concrete. At the end of the drives were two symmetrical 1930s semis. The houses were identical in design, colouring and detail. Each had a small, square front garden with a pocket handkerchief lawn bordered by beds of brightly coloured flowers. Either side of them, sections of rough grazing ground gave way to woods.

Stevenson opened his door and got out. He stretched his arms, the shoulders of his suit jacket bunching at the top, and then we were off down the drive of the house on the right. In the porch, he produced a key from his top pocket and unlocked the door. It opened with a swish across a thick, mauve carpet. The hall was narrow. At the far end was a kitchen lit by a window through which I glimpsed a garden in which a hundred colours blossomed. And then we were on the staircase to our left, its pale pink carpet as thick as the one on the floor. I followed Stevenson. At the top of the stairs, in a recess, there was a china cabinet filled with porcelain cups and saucers, the glass of its doors neatly outlined by diamonds of thin wood. On the left of the cabinet was a tiny, frosted window. Stevenson moved on to the landing.

Then he crept, slowly and quietly, into the bedroom at the front of the house. I followed him. We inched into the room. Sitting up in the bed was a little girl, about five or six years of age. She was combing the hair of a blonde-haired, blue-eyed doll wearing a frilly dress.

'Hello,' Stevenson said in a gentle voice, bending towards her.

The girl took her eyes off the doll for a second, looked at him and said 'Hello,' in a friendly voice. Then she returned to her grooming.

She wore a pale blue silk nightdress. A tiny pattern of pink roses had been picked out along the line of its buttons. Above her head, furry, pastel-coloured animals moved slowly around on a plastic carousel. Her bedspread was pale pink, her pillows brighter. Further shades of pink coloured her wallpaper, curtains and carpet. Underneath her windows were shelves filled with soft toys.

Stevenson was standing a respectful distance from the bed, as if in the presence of a princess.

'And where did you come from?' he asked.

'Pardon,' said the girl, still concentrating on her doll.

'Where did you come from?' Stevenson repeated.

She looked up at him and blinked.

'Where did your mummy get you?' Stevenson asked.

'She bought me in a shop.'

'And what did you cost?'

'Sixpence.'

'She must love you very much.'

'Yes. Mummy says I'm more precious than anything else in the world.'

I heard through the open door of the next room the sound of bedsprings moving up and down. And moaning – disguised but definite. The girl either couldn't hear them or was paying no attention. I reached over to her door and pushed it towards the frame.

'Do you know where babies come from?' asked Stevenson.

'They lie under bushes in blankets,' she replied, 'and you go and pick them up.'

I could hear a muffled woman's voice next door. I could make out what she was saying, though: 'You shouldn't have come so quickly.'

And then Stevenson was signalling that it was time to leave. As I followed him out of the room, I closed the girl's door behind me again. She was continuing to brush her doll's hair. She seemed happy enough.

Stevenson was in the bedroom next door. It was larger and mainly white with integrated wardrobes, twin chests of drawers and a dressing table on which a chunky mobile phone sat in a fat charger. A wide window at the back looked out on to a long garden. You could see the lawn next door, too. Beyond each garden was open countryside. Behind that was trees. And behind that, somewhere, must have been the Hall. Sitting up in the double bed and wearing a negligée, with the covers drawn up on her side but pushed away on the other, was Catherine. In front of her on the bed was a women's magazine open at an article headed, 'True blue – put a little sleaze into your love life'. Her hair was blonde and cut into a bob. She wore glasses with thin gold frames.

She looked up at me.

'Anonymous sex can bring me pleasure,' she said. 'It can brighten up my day and tone my body. But when it's with someone I love, I blossom.'

Her hair was messy. One of the straps of her negligée had slipped from her shoulder. She pointed to the room we had just come from.

'I took a vow of silence,' she said. 'To myself. I was six years old. Things had happened to me. Things I couldn't talk about, not even to my parents. Things I can't tell you. My psychiatrist was called Edward. He wore a dark suit with a gold chain. He smelt of ginger. I used to stare at his lips as they moved. I was living inside myself. It was right for me. I was giving myself tough love. I pushed everything outside my head and wouldn't let it back in.'

She reached over to a table by the side of her bed and picked a chocolate from an open box. Then she turned to the window, bit the sweet in two between her front teeth, and stared and sucked.

Stevenson motioned towards the door and led the way downstairs. We walked through the hall and into the kitchen.

The garden bloomed like a psychedelic feast through the window, its flowers swollen with sun and rain. The décor in the kitchen was very 1970s – brown vinyl worktops, chunky mixer taps, a hooded cream-coloured cooker, chrome bakelite toaster, orange, flowery curtains and wipe-clean wallpaper.

'Would you like some tea, sir?' Stevenson asked, opening a cupboard and removing a silver teapot.

'Er... OK,' I replied. I wasn't used to wandering into people's houses and making free with their stuff. But he seemed happy to take the responsibility.

I asked him whose house it was.

'Well, sir, you have already seen the young girl and the woman she has become. I dare say you will be introduced to more of the building's occupants.'

'What's your own place like, Stevenson?' I asked.

'My place, sir?'

'Yes, your apartment, your flat, rooms... whatever.'

'My room, sir, is with the other servants's quarters on the floor above your own suite. It is basic but functional.'

Shit – Stevenson living on the floor above me. Sitting up there, sleeping up there. Above my head. Maybe that room I had walked into was his? He must use that bathroom. How come I never meet him – or any of the others – on the staircase?

'Just the one room?' I asked.

'That form of accommodation was good enough for my

father, sir. And while I do not take after him in every respect, as you know, it is good enough for me.'

'Don't you want to live a bit more?'

'I am perfectly content with my lot, sir. There are not many people fortunate enough to live in a magnificent building designed by Vanburgh, and to wander at will through grounds designed by Capability Brown. It would surely be greedy to desire more.'

Stevenson had removed a silver spoon from a drawer and used it to give the teapot a quick stir. He produced a cloth from his pocket, dried the spoon, polished it and carefully put it back.

'Let us take our tea into the lounge, shall we, sir?' he said as he poured out the cups. I followed him in.

The lounge was well-lit by a bay window which looked out on to the garden. An open fireplace looked as though it would provide plenty of heat on a cold winter's day. Along the wall to our right was a black leather sofa. At the end nearest the window a girl sat, with her legs tucked underneath her. It was Catherine again. Her hair was up and she was wearing a scarlet ra-ra skirt. There was a bloom in her cheeks and she was snapping her fingers in time to a song she was singing – 'Girls on Film' by Duran Duran. There were two armchairs opposite the sofa, either side of the fireplace. Stevenson and I took one each. They had narrow wooden arm-rests and thin green cushions. We made ourselves as comfortable as we could. Above Catherine's head there was a reproduction of *The Haywain* by Constable. On the sofa next to her was a copy of *Smash Hits*.

'It's very nice here,' she said. 'Very nice. I've got everything I want. I feel safe. In the daytime the sun floods in through those windows. At night it's cosy by the fire. Sometimes, though, you can hear music coming through the walls from next door. They're not very thick. The boy next door's records – 'slash your wrists' music. We don't speak. A nod in the drive maybe. It would do him good to come round here, though – maybe even change his life.'

Yawning, she put a flat hand to her face.

119

'Ooh, sorry,' she said and giggled. 'I was out late last night. I'm not used to it. It was a good laugh.' She straightened her legs out in front of her and sat on the edge of the sofa, hands clasped in her lap. 'I've got to go now,' she said. 'Homework. Mum will kill me if I don't do it.'

She stood, slipped on a pair of pumps from the floor and flitted out. I looked at Stevenson. He was shaking his head and smiling gently.

'The youth of yesterday, sir. What will become of them?'

He looked at his watch.

'I believe, sir, that we have a few minutes. Would you like a glass of sherry?'

'Er… I don't know,' I said. 'I've never tried it. What's it like?'

'It is uncouth, sir, if you must know, but, like so many things, it must be sampled once.'

He had moved over to the other end of the room where there was a circular table on a single leg with a three-toed foot. There were various bottles on the table, of different shapes, sizes and colours, but Stevenson went straight for the one he wanted.

He came back with a small glass patterned with tiny opaque flecks. He handed it to me and I peered inside. It looked like piss. I sipped it – it tasted worse. Stevenson had a glass like mine, but it was already on the table next to him, with only a drop left at the bottom. I hadn't even seen him pour it, let alone drink it.

'Do you actually like this stuff, Stevenson?' I asked.

'Dear me, no, sir,' he replied. 'It is not my kind of thing at all. No, neat whisky is my tipple.'

Then we heard a low thudding come from the other side of the wall – and a hint of grouchy growling above it. It took a few seconds but then I recognised it – it was 'How I Wrote Elastic Man' by The Fall. Not exactly 'slash your wrists' music, but I could see why someone raised on *Smash Hits* might think it was. Stevenson was leaning back in his chair and staring into space, the whisky perhaps having chilled him out. His foot was tapping gently on the floor. We sat there, the two of us, for a minute or two, without speaking, and I must say it was quite pleasant. Then, as the record ended and another – something with a pounding piano and another thumping beat – began, Stevenson snapped himself out of his torpor and leaned forward again in his chair, angling himself towards me.

'Right, sir, shall we move on?'

We went back upstairs. This time we turned past the little girl's bedroom and into the one that sat alongside it at the front of the house. In here the curtains had been loosely drawn – like a dressing gown hastily pulled across a chest – and the atmosphere was gloomy. In the right-hand corner of the room was a bed. Catherine lay there, her face lit by a jagged triangle of light coming from from the uncovered part of the window. Her hair was thicker and longer now, waved and highlighted with blonde streaks. Her face was made up in greens and blues. There was some music in the background – something New Romantic. Maybe Visage. She was lying with her hands behind her head, staring at the ceiling. There were posters up there – Spandau Ballet, Culture Club, Bowie in a clown suit.

'Let me in, Joe,' she said quietly, 'Let me in and I'll take you where you've never been. I promise. Do it, Joe, let me in. You won't regret it. I know how you feel. I've seen it in your eyes. And that's how I feel, too. We're the same. Let's get away from here. Steal us a car, Joe. You've done that before – haven't you? We'll keep driving until we don't know where we are. Or who we are, any more. And then we'll stop. Because then we'll have arrived. I want my life to begin, Joe. Will you be the one to light the fuse? Are you the real thing, Joe? Or just another Martin? Fucking Martin. Thank you for fucking me, Martin – I hate you. Are you really what you said you are, Joe? Do you really have fire in your fingertips? Did you really do those things? Or are you lying to me? Just trying to impress me?'

She turned on to her side, facing us, squeezed her arm in between her legs and hugged herself. Then she closed her eyes.

Stevenson had taken hold of my arm and was leading me out of the room. He closed the door behind us and we went back downstairs.

This time we went straight to the front door and then we were outside again, in the driveway. We got back into the car.

We were putting on our seatbelts when we saw the front door of the house open. It was Catherine, pulling on a light coat. She came towards the car, then I heard the door behind me open and she was sitting behind me, smoothing the coat underneath her with one hand as she slammed the door with the other. The motor was already running. Stevenson performed a perfect three-point turn before taking us back in the direction we had come from.

I felt a hand on the back of my neck. It was Catherine. She was straightening the collar of my shirt. I turned and looked at her.

We spent the journey in silence. I watched her in the mirror – doing up her coat, brushing her hair, putting it in a ponytail. Then staring out of the window. She didn't give me a glance.

We stopped outside the cylindrical orange tower that we had passed yesterday. Maybe it was the trees behind, swaying in the wind, but it seemed to be leaning slightly to the left. The clouds were travelling past it in a line, as if they were on a conveyor belt. There was an open doorway to the tower – but no door. We walked in. The floor was littered with rubble of different sizes, some pieces as big as footballs. Inside the tower was a central stone staircase that wound its way up around a column that was like a spine. On the lower half of this spiral flight most of the steps were in reasonable condition but as I looked up I could see that some of those higher up were in a poor state and the ones towards the top had almost disintegrated.

Stevenson led the way, I followed, and Catherine brought up the rear. There was nothing to hold on to on that staircase – no handrail, no wall, nothing. By the time we were two thirds of the way up, chunks were missing from most of the steps, and some of them were barely half there. Finally we reached the top. All we had to do now was to take a couple of paces forward and we'd be on the platform that led to the last, tiny flight of stairs leading to the roof. But we would never take those couple of paces – because the floor there had completely vanished. There was just air between us and the platform –

and a void below. Stevenson gathered himself and sprang. He landed agilely on the other side. Without breaking his stride he carried on, grit crunching under his feet, on to the second flight of stairs. Segment by segment, his body disappeared on to the roof. I was looking ahead of me, concentrating on the spot where he had landed, trying not to think of the vast black hole falling away like a well beneath my feet. The distance to jump was tiny, the distance to fall huge. I could feel Catherine's eyes on my back. I concentrated and leapt. I landed – and scrambled away, reaching out, half-bent, for the next set of stairs. Then I turned round – and Catherine skipped across behind me as if she was hopping over a crack on the pavement.

Stevenson was already up on the roof when I started up that second flight. As I reached the top, I could see that there was someone else up there, too. I climbed out on to the parapet – both the wall round the edge and the sky above looked wonderfully solid – and saw the actor who had played Chuck and Ed. He was looking over the wall, hands spread across its rim, across to the trees. Catherine came up behind me. I moved aside. She walked over to the actor and stood next to him. Stevenson, with his back to me, held up his arm. I stayed where I was. In the centre of the roof, on a raised stone platform, was the statue I had first seen from the jeep the day before. It was an ancient Greek, naked apart from a cloak draped around his shoulders and falling behind him. He had a tiny dick, curly hair and a middle-age spread. In one hand he held a set of scales, in the other a wine jug.

Catherine was talking to the actor.

'It's all over, Joe,' she said. 'You weren't quite how I'd imagined, you know. But that was my fault, of course.' She balanced on her toes and looked over the wall. 'Look down,' she said. 'Right down. To where the wall meets the ground. Lean right over. So far that you think you might fall. Maybe it's not too late for you, after all.' But Joe wasn't listening – he was staring straight ahead, towards the horizon. 'See how brave you really are, Joe. Maybe you can win me back. I've only ever seen you pretend, Joe. I've never seen anything real from you. Well, maybe you can fool the rest of them but you can't fool me. You're all the same. None of you dares to reach out that little bit further to touch the truth. You're just an actor, Joe. You don't deserve me.'

Joe peeled away from the wall and pushed past Stevenson and me on to the steps. He took them in one jump. I looked down after him. He sprang easily across the drop and landed, braced firmly, on the other side. Then down he went, two steps at a time towards the ground, feet pounding on the stone. But Catherine wasn't watching. She hadn't seen him being brave.

We followed him down, Stevenson leading and Catherine next this time. I watched them jump and land. Stevenson was light on his feet for a big man, Catherine springy like a sapling. They could have been a pair of ballet dancers. It went OK for me this time – I think it was because Catherine wasn't behind, watching me.

By the time we got to the bottom, Joe had vanished. Stevenson moved over to the car and I followed but Catherine stopped to smoke a cigarette.

'Right we are, sir,' Stevenson said to me, standing in front of the bonnet. 'I trust that was informative. Let's move on, shall we?'

Catherine stood like a dreamy French film star, staring towards the woods and the Viscount's Arch. Her left arm was flat across her chest, her right upright, smoke drifting away from it in the breeze like a miniature, sallow version of the trail of clouds behind the tower.

I climbed into the passenger seat as Stevenson moved round to the driver's side. He paused there for a moment before he got in and I could see Catherine looking our way. Then he opened the door and she put out her cigarette and started heading towards us. Stevenson started the car and then Catherine was climbing in to the back seat. Once she was in, she reached over to her right, picked up an expensive looking carrier bag from the floor, and put it in her lap. And then we were off again, skimming over the grass.

We turned back on to the road, but almost immediately stopped once more. On our left, on top of a gentle hill, was a kind of mini-version of the Hall – minus the colonnades –

a temple with thick columns and a squashed pyramid for a portico. We walked across the grass towards it, Stevenson and I in front, Catherine tailing behind. The door was unlocked. Stevenson opened it and I followed him in. It was gloomy in the hallway. We took a doorway immediately to our right and emerged into a light, airy drawing room. In the middle was a grand piano, with its lid down. Its keyboard, though, was open and some sheet music was spread across an ornate wooden stand. In front of the piano there was a line of four stiff-backed chairs, white with light-blue velvet cushions, and back rests pulled tight into their frames. There was a light creak from the floorboards as we walked in. Particles of dust sparkled as they revolved in the light by the window. Stevenson motioned me towards the chairs. I sat down, assuming that Catherine would join me. But she didn't come. She had disappeared.

And then Stevenson sat down on the piano stool – and began to play. And that wasn't the most surprising thing – it was what he was playing. While his left hand pounded out a two-chord reggae rhythm, his right played a bouncy, immediately recognisable melody, ornamented with some baroque flourishes. It was Althea and Donna's 'Uptown Top Ranking' – a celebration of teenage life in Trenchtown, and a number one back in the late seventies. On Black Box Recorder's *England Made Me* it was transposed from Kingston, Jamaica to Kingston, Surrey. Stevenson in his tails was skanking solidly at the keyboard – laying down a rocksteady beat against the atmosphere of the thick pile carpet, the candelabra and the gilt cornices. It was quite a sight, and quite a sound in that environment – sweet and sour, a chocolate orange, Guinness and black. Towards the end of the piece, Stevenson slowed the beat, before finishing with a series of jagged two-handed chords. I applauded immediately – and perhaps a little wildly. Stevenson gave me a warning look. I toned it down. He seemed to appreciate that and nodded slowly at me. Then he stood up. I thought I saw the tiniest hint of a smile on his face.

'One must keep one's hand in, sir. The fingers must continue to fly across the keys. Right, they should be ready for us by now.'

We went back out into the hall and then up a staircase at the far end. Halfway up, where a square, white-framed window was set into the wall, the stairs turned on themselves and climbed back towards the front of the building.

Up at the top it was very quiet, as if the carpet there was lining the walls and the ceiling as well as the floor. At the far end of the corridor there was another square window, in the same position as the one directly below it. This one had a bowl of dried crimson flowers in it. Stevenson was halfway into a room on our left. I followed him. He closed the door behind me.

The room was almost in darkness. I was reminded straight away of the scene in Tombstone when Catherine had been menaced by the Kid. As my eyes grew accustomed to the gloom, though, this room looked very different. It was furnished expensively but not extravagantly – whoever lived here had plenty of money but taste, too. The only light came from the far end. There, a gauzy hint of daylight was visible round the rectangular outline of the blind that was closed against the window. Grey and white flickers from a portable television palely lit the face of a figure lying on a sofa – Catherine.

Stevenson moved forward and I followed him.

He walked towards the sofa and Catherine swung her legs off and sat up to make room for him. She was wearing a thick white cardigan and she pulled it round her, hugging herself. I sat on an armchair at the end of the sofa. On the television there was some footage of the Falklands War – soldiers running across a field pimpled with tiny khaki mounds, a couple of sheep in the background, and then a figure in glasses speaking to camera. Catherine had the sound turned down but I recognised him from old news clips – it was the government PR guy who used to give the spin on all the things the viewers weren't allowed to see for themselves.

'England on a Sunday,' said Catherine. 'Is there anything worse? Is there anything so horribly, drably familiar? Do you think the Anglo-Saxons stayed in bed on Sundays, animal skin blankets pulled over their heads?'

She pointed at the television.

'Don't worry. It's the other side of the world. It can't touch you. Men with guns, men with bayonets. Explosions. But all the deaths happen off-screen. The stretcher bearers go the long way round to avoid the cameras. It's nothing to worry about.'

She picked up a cup on the table by the sofa, took a sip, scowled and put it back again.

'Mummy phoned.' She angled her head to one side. 'You'll be glad to know that she's fine.' She moved her head upright again. 'What else did she say? Oh, I don't know. I can't remember. Oh – Andrew called as well.' Stevenson gave a knowing chuckle but she paid him no attention. 'He wants money.' Stevenson laughed out loud this time. I stared at him. 'Money,' she continued. 'But that's all any of us care about now, isn't it? There's no such thing as society, Mrs Thatcher says. Well, in that case, why should there be any such thing as the family? Write off one, Margaret, and you'll find yourself writing off the other, too. Your precious English family - it'll be dead.'

Stevenson nodded.

'Andrew'll get nothing from me,' Catherine said. 'Anyway, it serves him right. Investments can go down as well as up. Doesn't he read his own small print? Well, I intend to do what I'm told by Maggie. I'm actively seeking my fortune. For God, England and St Margaret. What time is it?'

Stevenson showed her his watch.

'Shit,' she said. 'Already. Sunday night is hell – knowing that tomorrow it all starts again. It might as well be Monday morning already.'

She sank back into the sofa and folded her arms across her stomach, her legs slightly apart. For a moment she looked almost middle-aged.

'Oh, yes,' she added as an afterthought. 'Jane phoned, too. She's in hospital again. Don't ask. She wants me to go and see her. Maybe I'll go next Sunday. Or maybe I'll try and persuade Mummy to go. She could do with some real misery in her life – it might give her a sense of perspective.'

As her head sank into her chest, Stevenson was already on his feet.

I joined him and we left Catherine to her Sunday evening.
On our way back down the stairs I said:

'I take it you're no Thatcherite then, Stevenson?'

'It is fortunate that we British have so much else to be proud
of, is it not, sir?'

'Does your patriotism come from your dad?' I asked as we
reached the bottom and began to head for the front door, light
slanting in through its glass.

'Very much so, sir,' he said, striding along the narrow strip
of royal-blue carpet. 'Although I would have to say that my
father was more of an English patriot than a British one. He
never ventured over those borders to west and north, sir, in
the whole of his life, and the Irish Sea might as well have
been the Pacific to him. As he once said to me: "Why would
anyone living in the Garden of Eden ever want to leave it?" I
believe, sir, that, in his innocence, the idea of worldliness and
otherworldly temptation never entered his head.'

Stevenson had finished his speech standing outside a door
opposite the drawing room. He opened it and we went in.

We were in a lounge. The carpet was cream, there was a glass
bowl full of dried pampas grass in front of the window, a low
cappuccino-coloured sofa and, above a shiny grey fireplace,
an oil painting of an old frigate fighting a mid-ocean storm,
poop deck buried underneath a veil of spray. Stevenson moved
over to the window and stood there, hands clasped behind his
back. He looked like a school teacher, sure enough of his hold
over his class to turn his back on them. He seemed to be lost
in contemplation – perhaps he was thinking of his father? –
and I left him to it. I wandered round the room. The carpet
looked recently vacuumed, the magazines on the glass table
were piled neatly on top of each other and the books on the
shelves – Victorian and Modernist novels, books on European
cookery and far eastern travel – were arranged by size, rather
than author, genre or subject matter.

In the corner there was a bureau with an old-fashioned
inkstand at one end and a blank pad of writing paper set
squarely in the middle. There was a slight curl to the top page,
as if there had recently been another on top, filled with words.

I picked up the pad. There were indentations there. I tilted it slightly so that the light caught them. There was something pretty heavy going on at the bottom of the page – several underlinings and something, possibly 'fuck you', in capitals – but I didn't get the chance to examine it any more because Stevenson was talking to me and his voice had a certain edge to it.

'I think we should sit down now, sir – over here,' he said.

He still had his arms behind his back but he was looking straight at me, his legs slightly apart. I tossed the pad back on to the desk and went to join him. He watched me all the way and only when I had sat down at one end of the sofa did he take a seat at the other.

'How old are you, Stevenson?' I whispered to him.

'Old enough to be your father, sir,' he replied and shifted his attention immediately to the door, which had just opened. It was the other actress. She walked slowly across the room towards us. The raincoat that she undid as she moved was wet and so was her hair. I looked instinctively towards the window, but of course it was still dry out there. Stevenson gave me a disappointed look. The actress threw the raincoat on to a chair and sat down on another that was opposite us. She stretched out the fingers of one hand and looked down at her nails. Then she looked straight in front of her – at a point on the sofa halfway between Stevenson and me.

'It's over,' she said. 'He meant everything to me. Give me a death in the family instead – I could handle that. I'd trade any one of them for him in a second.'

On the table next to her were bottles of gin and tonic. She mixed a stiff one and swallowed half in one go. Running her hand through her hair and pulling it tight, she said:

'Every time he took hold of me the last few weeks it was the same thing. The same stale looks, the same dead moves. Nowhere to go, no way out. He was leaving and I couldn't stop him. Nothing lasts, they say.'

She looked up at me.

'But we had good times. There's plenty to remember. And nothing to regret.'

129

She finished her drink and poured herself another one.

'And anyway, I've already got my eye on someone else. He's an older man.'

She looked at Stevenson.

'A richer man, too, as it happens,' she continued. 'That was just one of those things. You make your own luck, don't you?'

Stevenson, eyebrows puckered and cheeks drawn in, nodded.

'He likes me, I know he does. I can tell. When it happens, I just know.'

She looked at her watch.

'I need to pop out,' she said and stood up, taking another swig from her glass.

Turning to Stevenson, she said:

'How do I look?'

'Exceptionally beautiful, ma'am,' Stevenson replied.

She smiled brightly and nodded at him.

She whisked up her raincoat on her way to the door and twirled it through the air before wrapping it round her shoulders and pushing her arms through the sleeves.

I looked across at Stevenson.

'Would you like a little reading matter while we wait, sir?' he asked.

I had begun to say, "No, you're all right", but it was too late – he'd already whipped a magazine from the table on his left into his right hand and then on to the sofa next to me. I picked it up. It was one of those 'homes of the celebrities' magazines. Haines was on the cover.

He was leaning across some kind of antique tea trolley and smiling at the camera. The headline was 'Duke Luke'. I turned to the relevant page and there was Haines again, this time with a big grin on his face as he stood inside the door of the south entrance of the Hall and, with one arm spread towards the Viscount's Arch, showed off the huge lawn and the lake. There was an interview, too. It started with a badly informed summary of his career and was followed by a series of inane questions, which he answered in his usual style.

There were plenty more pictures of Haines on the next pages, outside and inside various temples, reclining on one arm on the front lawn and even punting a boat down the river. No more agency photos for this rag – they must have paid him a fortune. There were ironic quotes from him, too, to go with the pictures. I remember a couple:

'I wanted your readers to see where a life dedicated to self-gratification, contempt and a refusal to work could get them.'

'Some days I lie in my four-poster bed, surrounded by Old Masters and Louis Quatorze furniture, as the maid draws my bath, and think how lucky I have been. But I soon put that s--- out of my head. I f----ing deserve this!'

At the end of the article, in a small box, it said 'Next month: We meet Catherine, the elegant Mrs Haines.'

As I finished flicking through the article, the door opened again. The actress came back in. I put the magazine carefully back on the sofa. She was carrying a baby.

The actress went over to the same chair and sat down again, putting the baby on her knee. She ignored us completely – it was as if we weren't there – and spoke only to the little kid.

'I'm going to love you so much. Take care of you. I'm going to call you David. You're mine now. I've met a man, he's going to be your daddy – we're going to be a family. He'll be here soon. He's going to love you, too. We're all going to love each other. He'll look after us, support us. We'll all be safe together.'

Her voice had begun to slow towards the end. When she stopped speaking, her grip began to slacken around the baby. I reached forward but Stevenson's hands got there before me. He scooped the baby up with one arm and then put it on his own knee, where he bounced it up and down gently. It began to gurgle contentedly. The actress slumped back on to the sofa. Her eyes closed.

Stevenson and I looked at each other.

'One must never exaggerate the extent of the pressures that were heaped on to our young women at the end of the previous millennium, sir.'

'Yes, I suppose you're right,' I said, eyes on the actress.

'Margaret Thatcher has so much to answer for, sir, would you not agree?'

'That woman destroyed whole communities and whole industries, Stevenson.'

'And we are still paying the price today, sir, are we not?'

'North Sea oil, the selling off of council houses. A culture of selfishness and greed.'

'Indeed, sir,' said Stevenson. 'How can one trust a woman who removes a bottle of milk from a child's mouth and demands money for its return?'

'I never figured you as a socialist, Stevenson.'

'I see myself more as an apolitical egalitarian, sir. Someone who likes to see a level playing field. A meritocrat.'

He was patting the baby gently on the back.

'I take it you weren't exactly following in your father's footsteps there, Stevenson?' I ventured.

'You are correct, sir. Father was one of the old school. He believed in a kind of paternalist feudalism. He did what he was told by his masters and that included adopting their political views wholesale.'

'There are some people who would find it difficult to reconcile your egalitarianism and your patriotism.'

'I see no reason to regard those two ideals as mutually exclusive, sir. Far from it. I believe them, in fact, to be mutually dependent.'

Our little political discussion was interrupted by a knock at the door.

'Ah,' Stevenson said and, hoisting the baby on to his shoulder, got up and walked across the room.

He opened the door and passed the baby through. Then he came back again.

'I think we should leave the lady, sir, don't you? An officer is due here shortly to interview her.'

I followed Stevenson out. The corridor was empty. We left the building and made our way back towards the car.

'I think there's something coming through on the radio,' Stevenson said, standing by the open passenger door. 'Shall we take a listen? It's a short-wave radio, sir. I find it useful in all sorts of ways.'

He bent down and flicked a switch. We listened together as we stared across the peaceful green fields below the pale blue sky.

A man's voice came through, coated in a thin layer of static and punctuated by crackles, the message bookended by clicks.

'I see her, sarge. We've got her under surveillance – she's heading north.'

Another voice burst across him.

'This is more than a little domestic, constable. There's a place for this woman reserved on the front page of every tabloid in the land! Get after her! Switch your siren on!'

'Yes, sir.'

The radio went silent. I looked at Stevenson but he was staring into space again.

The radio burst back into life. The constable sounded breathless.

'We've got her, sarge,' he said, 'we've got her.'

'Congratulations, constable,' was the sarcastic response. 'Well, what does she have to say for herself?'

'She's not making any sense, sarge. I don't think she understands the trouble she's in. She keeps going on about some bloke she loves.'

'The cuffs, constable,' came the response. 'Bring her in.'

Stevenson reached down to turn off the transmission.

'I think we'll be needed upstairs again now, sir,' he said. 'We need to find out what happens to this unfortunate woman's sister. Maybe we can hope for something better for her, sir?'

As we walked back towards the house I noticed that Catherine's curtains upstairs had been opened.

Back on the top floor, her room looked very bare in the light. White walls with cream cornices. Narrow lines, vertical and horizontal, thin gauzes and cloths drawn tight, tied and pinned. No stains, no indentations, no dust, no dirt. No decoration apart from a long, rectangular painting in the centre of one of the walls – an abstract in whites and dark blues that looked like the lights of a city reflected in water.

Catherine was wearing a grey cashmere twinset and pearls. She was sitting at a desk – similar to the other actress's a floor below – and she had been writing something. She pushed it to one side as we came in. She turned to face us, crossing her legs, once we'd sat down on the sofa.

'England made me,' she said, looking from Stevenson to me and then back again. 'England made me. Just as it made you, Stevenson.'

She looked at me again. It was an aristocratic look.

'I'm not sure about you,' she said. 'Not yet.'

'As a girl,' she continued, 'I was already a little English lady, fully formed. I was well brought up. I was told what was important. I was taught wrong from right. And how to get what I wanted.' She looked away for a second. 'Maybe I forgot some of it for a while, but it's all come back to me now.'

'It's not something you can ever lose,' she continued, her nails tapping on her desk now like knitting needles. 'The English lady's survival instinct is inextinguishable. And our defence can easily turn into attack. We English do love a good murder, don't we? The crueller the killing the better. But it should be coolly done. Coldly callous. We turn up our noses a little at frenzied attacks, don't we? They lack refinement and taste. Murder should be premeditated and well planned. It should be carried out clinically.'

She reached round to the back of her neck and adjusted her necklace.

'Damned thing,' she said. 'Keeps trapping my hair.'

She settled again.

'Daddy taught me how important it is to have secrets. And Mummy showed me how to keep them. Every English lady is a double agent. Not very patriotic, you might think. Well, tell that to the royal family and the Cambridge spies. Tell that to those pillars of our establishment.'

She reached into a handbag that was by her feet, took out a bottle of perfume and dabbed it on to each wrist.

'That's better,' she said. 'There's something almost spiritual about Chanel No 5. My daughter says she can't stand it, but I know she'll come round. I was the same at her age. We're so alike.'

She stared hard at me.

'It's been two months now,' she continued. 'Since they took her. Since they took my little girl.'

There was a hollow look in her eyes.

'I know she's an heiress,' she continued, 'but deep down inside she's just a little girl. Arthur says he won't pay. He says it's too much money. His own daughter. Of course he can pay!'

She shook her head. There were tears in her eyes.

'I want to tell her I love her. I just want her to know.' She looked at me. 'She doesn't know.'

She heaved a sigh.

'I thought everything was going to be all right,' she said. 'I thought I'd finally found a life for myself. After all the stumbling around. I thought I'd finally ended up on my feet. Money. Security. Love. A family. I had it all. Everything I wanted. Everything I needed.'

She got up from the sofa and moved stiffly to the window. She closed the curtains and then came back to her chair again in the gloom. I knew it was time to go – I was already halfway up when Stevenson gave me the signal.

Back outside again, we got straight into the car this time.

'And what's your impression of the psyche of the English female, Stevenson?' I asked.

'I really don't see that it is my place to philosophise, or worse still pontificate, on that particular subject, sir.'

'Is there a Mrs Stevenson?' I asked with a smile. 'Or perhaps a lady who would like to become Mrs Stevenson?'

'Piss off!' Stevenson roared, laughing so much that I thought he was going to lose control of the wheel. Then suddenly he stopped and turned to face me.

'No, I mean it,' he said. 'Piss off.'

He turned back to the road. I had obviously overstepped the mark. And I had only myself to blame. I should have known better than to enquire about the private life of a gentleman's gentleman.

We were about to pass the wrecked car again. The actress

was lying on the ground next to it – exactly as we had left her. She didn't even give us a glance as we went by. But Stevenson pulled over. He was back in his easygoing mood.

'It looks as though that young lady still has part of her tale to tell, sir, wouldn't you say? Shall we go and hear it?'

We got out and walked back towards the car.

When we were right in front of her, she yawned, stretched out her arms and sat up. After looking at each of us, she began to speak.

'"We're going to turn you into a woman. You won't be a girl any more." That's what they told me at the farm. It was quite a shock, I can tell you. I'd enjoyed being a child and I wanted to carrying on being one. Being a girl. But by then I knew it was already too late. I'd seen too much – heard too much. "We're going to turn you into someone new. You won't even remember who you once were. You'll be one of us. One with us. You'll risk your life for us." It was so romantic! I loved it. I loved them. I've looked it up – they call it Stockholm Syndrome. But it's not. It's love. They gave me a sub-machine gun. It was so heavy I could hardly hold it, but they showed me how. I'm wearing a camouflage jacket and a bullet belt in the photos. I look good. They were going to send them out. To the newspapers. Television. There are some copies in here somewhere.' She looked around her. 'It's all such a mess. Maybe you could have a look? It's the way I'd like to be remembered, you see. As having done something with my life. Would you do that for me?'

Without waiting for a reply she yawned and stretched again, before lying down on the ground, in the same position as before, arms posed theatrically.

Stevenson shook his head sorrowfully and began to move off again towards the car. I called to him:

'Shouldn't we look? For the photos?'

He turned round and looked at me.

'Yes, sir, I suppose we should,' he said. 'We should respect the young lady's final wish.'

I stepped over the actress and opened the back door of the car. In the well was a canvas bag and on the seat was a briefcase, half open. It looked as though it had once been on the rear shelf and had been hurled against the headrests at the front in the collision. I opened it. I picked through a handful of travel brochures and then a series of documents in German before I found them. There were about twenty copies of the same photo. It was pretty much as the actress had described it, except that she was also wearing a short skirt, high heels and bright red lipstick. I grabbed them and held them up to Stevenson.

'Jolly good, sir,' he said. 'Shall we go now?'

Editor's note —

It looks as though the writer may have been tired by his authorial exertions – or by the movement of events over the course of the day. His account ends without any of the usual culinary details or musings on the whereabouts of Stevenson. Yes, that good officer was absent from supper once again this evening – things are proceeding apace. Well, the writer is going to need to summon some energy from somewhere.

Right. Rewind.

Stevenson is very happy with the Daimler inherited from his recently deceased father. But he aspires to own a Standard Bentley S.2 saloon – it is the car stolen by Billy in *Seance on a Wet Afternoon* and used to kidnap the rich man's daughter. Billy himself would like to own a Rolls Royce – and has been promised one by Myra once they have successfully completed their plan. Billy is particularly impressed by the 'fact' that the loudest thing in the Rolls as it purrs along is the sound of the clock. That is also the only noise to be heard in the lounge once Myra's gramophone has ceased its blaring.

Ah, the legend – or should I say myth – of the gamekeeper who blew out his brains for love of his Lady. So she was bored with life here in the Garden of Eden and led him on, did she? And he, a mere hired hand of the Earl, had been either innocent or stupid enough to believe that she really felt something for him? A likely story.

As time goes by it becomes more and more obvious how pale a shadow the writer casts in comparison with the family whose portraits surround him at various points of his day. Literally so when he is compared with the first Earl and his son. The second Earl was a more corpulent man even than his father and loved huntin', shootin' and fishin' – and dining at length on the ripe, red, stinking fruit brought to him by his dogs, guns and rods. Once, when out hunting, he fell from his horse into a ditch and became wedged there. Ropes were tied around his wrists and ankles and when he finally emerged no little time later, caked with mud and dripping wet, a fusillade of expletives barrelling from his mouth, he resembled nothing more than the trussed and defeated boar which he had imagined accompanying his return from his expedition. Maybe he was aware of this. On his return he charged through the front door of the Hall. His poor wife retreated from him as he stampeded through the doors and corridors and up the stairs of their home, but she was unable to lock her chamber in time and he burst it open, sending her sprawling on the floor. He proceeded to follow her, on all fours, pulling off his dirt-festooned clothes, snorting like a pig, until he cornered her and she was forced to succumb to his porcine charms. His humiliation in the ditch and the frustration of his murderous designs on the hunting field were then sublimated in a sexual act.

Fortunately for the Earl's wife, she was to outlive him by many years. After his death from over-eating at the age of fifty she managed to produce from somewhere a codicil to his will which revealed his desire to be buried next to the pig sty housing his beloved collection of porkers. It was surely not the good Lady's fault that said animals managed – in the fullness of time – to break down the fence of their pen, dig through a wall of mud, batter their way through the side of the Earl's coffin and devour his remains. And anyway, he loved those pigs so much, surely he would have been happy for his final act on this earth to have been the provision of such a delicious meal for them?

The writer admits to being lulled to sleep at night by the noise of the generator in the power yard. More evidence of mental weakness – pull yourself together, man! The writer's choice of lullaby is surely an indication of his unconscious surrender to the power of the house – and therefore to Mr Haines himself. Indeed, that sound could almost be the amplified purring of the master.

The writer has had to do without lunch again. Anyone would think he is being deprived of food on purpose.

Yes, Stevenson's father was an interesting man. But that is another story and there remains too little of the day to tell it. We must concentrate on other things.

Plenty of acting today – I like to see that. Young girls with expectations put upon them become adolescents with issues who become young women with dreams of leaving. Some of them live out those dreams while others become depressed and others find their dreams turning to nightmares. And England, dear England, the island we love so much, is responsible for everything. England, which had to allow Hitler to rise in order to defeat him, which had to allow Argentina to invade the Falklands in order to sail to their rescue.

England Made Me, the first album by Black Box Recorder, Mr Haines's side project of the mid-to-late nineties. With the heat of his previous artistic conflagrations still singeing the turntables of Britain, Mr Haines put the Auteurs on ice and, in collaboration with his friend Mr John Moore, began writing frosty songs about the cold Britain of the late nineties (thank you for everything, John Major). Songs from the point of view of a young woman. So never let it be said that Mr Haines neglects the ladies. He even found one to sing the new material for him – Sarah Nixey. Mr Haines had recently given up working on *ESP Kids*, a concept album about 'feral gangs of telekinetic youths' and had decided that after *Murder Park* and *Baader Meinhof* he wanted something a bit less confrontational, something that would allow him to stand back a bit from the world he had created. And show his gentler side. Mr Haines relished his new disguise. He even deigned to appear on *Top of the Pops*. To promote a hit single that he and Mr Moore had tossed off.

Mr Haines and Mr Moore have been accused – would you Adam and Eve it? – of being upper-middle-class ex-public schoolboys. When in fact everyone knows that they are surviving twins of working-class Seventh Day Adventist mothers and devil-worshipping fathers.

But let us catch up on a little more history while we are here:

On August 1st Noel Gallagher accepted the poisoned chalice rejected by Damon Albarn and visited Tony Blair at Downing Street, along with Creation boss Alan McGee. By now, though, Noel G had deserted Camden – and the infrequent company of Mr Haines – for the shires. On August 31st Princess Diana died. (Black Box Recorder would later use Elton John's sublime tribute to her, 'Candle in the Wind 1997' as intro music for one of their public performances). In November Creation Records was wound up. Mr Haines was running out of friendly neighbours – although Messrs Robert Plant and Jimmy Page had attended his thirtieth birthday celebrations in October. The ghost of Aleister Crowley must have hovered close by that night.

Stevenson is correct. All entry and exit points to the estate are sealed. No one arrives or leaves without Mr Haines's say-so. The walls are cemented with broken glass. The river is metal-fenced and spiked. And the electronic highway is barricaded by a blazing firewall.

There is a quiet certainty to the misconceptions – if I may be excused the term – of the little girl in the bed. Her mother says that she is 'more precious than anything else in the world'. 'Precious' is what Myra, the would-be child killer in *Seance on a Wet Afternoon*, was called by her own mother. It is also how she addresses the spirit of her stillborn son, Arthur, who she believes to be instructing her actions. Myra – disguised in a face mask as 'Nurse Johnson' – is wrongfooted by the brightness of the girl she and Billy have kidnapped, who knows more about medical procedures than Myra does. Billy, masked, too, is bamboozled by her as well. But she is still a little girl, she still has her misconceptions – Billy cannot be a doctor, she says, because doctors smell 'all pepperminty'. And Billy has the smell of fear on his breath.

Stevenson's room. Bare. Functional. No frills. A monk's cell. Yes, it is the room the writer stepped inside. And the way he saw it is exactly how Stevenson keeps it. It was not necessary to change anything for the writer's visit. Yes, Stevenson uses that bathroom. That is all I can say on the subject. I am not familiar with the style or content of his ablutions. Although I have a feeling that a coarse flannel and coal tar soap may be involved. Why does the writer never meet any of the servants on the stairs? Because they have their own staircase. They must be able to provide immediate service to Mr Haines whenever he requires it.

Ah, Mr Haines makes an invisible – but certainly not inaudible – appearance as the boy next door! What a rambunctious rapscallion, turning the record player up to eleven like that!

How considerate of Stevenson to educate the writer into the charms of the sherry bottle. And how is he rewarded? By being himself accused of consuming said 'beverage'! The very thought caused me to spill my Chateau Lafite '53 down my shirt front. Bastard writer – one glass of this stuff is worth more than he has earned in any year of his life. Not to mention the laundry bill. Do not worry, though – he will pay.

The writer enjoys a few minutes' silence in the company of Stevenson. This is a touching moment. Even if Stevenson was probably miles away – dreaming perhaps of that special person who will one day become 'Mrs Stevenson'.

The walk up the broken stairs of the tower reminds one of the darkened walk up the staircase inside the warehouse to meet the second light aircraft on fire. But where that earlier journey was only imagined by the writer to be dangerous, this one is genuinely life-threatening. How thoughtful of Stevenson to be providing such a fully rounded experience for him. And here was the substitute warming up on the touchline, jogging up and down, all ready should he be called upon!

A tiny dick, a middle-aged spread, a set of scales and a wine jug. My guide book is reticent on the subject, so my best guess is that this was some Ancient Journalist.

Stevenson's ivory tinkling is a genuine surprise. I honestly had no idea of his capabilities in this field. Is there no end to his accomplishments? Give that man a pay rise, I say. No, wait a minute, steady on...

The English Sunday. In *Seance on a Wet Afternoon*, this was when Myra, as a young girl, was called upon to demonstrate her psychic powers to the family gathered downstairs.

'Andrew called. He wants money.' A private joke. Andrew is the name of Stevenson's stockbroker. Stevenson is always complaining about how he constantly has to wire extra funds to him in order to take full advantage of the latest insider information. Stevenson does not trust Andrew (obviously – he is a stockbroker) and syphons his winnings from his current account to a deposit account as soon as his gains have been made.

Maybe the writer is gradually waking from his Rip Van Winkle-like somnolence. He notices the indented paper on the pad. This could have been a bad moment for Stevenson, whose note to Mary regarding her failure to reset the camera in the writer's room had been torn from there. Fortunately for Stevenson, though – for whom the sack and therefore a total disintegration of the life he has so carefully built up, was at this point a very real prospect – he was able to step in quickly and remove the writer from the danger area. Mr Haines is a considerate and fair employer but a mistake like this, should it have led to discovery of his plans, would, I can guarantee you, have resulted in Stevenson's immediate dismissal.

The writer asks Stevenson his *age*...

Yes, a certain amount of money did change hands in order for the visit of the photographer and 'journalist' from the celebrity homes magazine to take place. There was, however, another motive behind the decision to briefly allow these dogs to shit and trample their way through the grounds of the Hall. What this magazine bought were sole, one-off rights. As a result, the other packs of media hounds will have to cease their baying and troop away, tails between their legs.

Ah yes, the interview in the magazine. I provide a brief taste:

'How did you feel when you first set foot in this marvellous, marvellous place?'

'I was coked up to the eyeballs, darling – you could have shown me a tenement in the Gorbals and it would have looked the same to me.'

'What's it like to be lord of the manor?'

'Well, it gives me a chance to preserve a few ancient customs – like *droit de seigneur* and flogging the peasants.'

Etc., etc.

Miss Françoise. Yes, it is high time that this dear lady – who, I should now add, has been Catherine's companion at the Hall from the earliest days with the Texan Mr Griff – was named. Apologies, ma'am, for leaving this recognition so late. Miss Françoise poured out all her affection and hopes in the little scene with baby 'David'. It was a good thing Stevenson was there to catch the tiny chap when he fell. For, it must be said, this part was not in the script.

Stevenson says he has other uses for his short-wave radio. I am not sure what he means by this. Whatever they are, I am sure they are valid.

The writer attempts to get Stevenson to comment on the 'psyche of the English female' – an invitation which Stevenson cleverly deflects. But the writer should have saved his breath. As he should know, all the necessary work on this subject has already been done for us – by Messrs Haines and Moore on the *England Made Me* record. A remarkable achievement for two heterosexual males, and a task not many men in this land would be willing to take on – because it is a subject in which few of them have any interest. Clean socks, tea on the table at six, sex on a Sunday night, the freedom to piss it up down the pub every other evening of the week – these are still their main concerns. In some ways the demands on the English female are no less onerous now than they have ever been.

The probing of Stevenson's private life by the writer, jocular or not, was a bad mistake. But he seems to have learnt from it. I hope so, for his sake. Stevenson has his dignity. He also has the wherewithal – and the permission – to defend it.

It is unfortunate that the writer has still not been able to make it into Mr Haines's inner sanctum for an interview with the man. He would have seen many wondrous things there, including new versions, painted by Mr Haines himself – it is good to see that the months at art college in Portsmouth were not wasted, after all – of Rubens' *Peasants in a Barn* and *Peasants Going to Market*. Suffice to say that the impoverished men and ladies depicted here are occupying themselves in ways that would bring tears even to Mr Rubens' well-travelled eyes. The writer would also have made acquaintance, on this fictitious visit we have conjured up for him, with the portrait of the Marquess, father of the first Earl. There is still a twinkle in the old chap's eye after all these years.

After retiring from his lucrative position at the Board of Trade – in order, it was alleged, to take up a better paid one as sequesterer and diverter of his ageing wife's funds – the Marquess became something of a recluse. He devoted himself to his temples and their dedication to the twin values of Arcadianism and freemasonry – and particularly to the form of the latter known as the 'Egyptian rite', promulgated by Cagliostro. Various other members of the landed gentry joined him in this adherence to the creed of the Grand Copt, and in his book, *All This is Ours*, the Marquess was liberal in his descriptions of their nefarious activities in the grounds of the Hall. The book was printed on the same press at the Hall that would later see the production of programmes for the first Earl's harmless theatricals, and slim volumes of his romantic poetry. The Marquess's book was limited to a print run of only ten – it was intended purely for the delectation of his inner circle. The accounts of his hopes to discover new colours and new dyes, and of his almost light-hearted search for the Philosopher's Stone (it kept him busy as the builders toiled on his temples) were harmless enough, but the frolicking with naked servant girls plied with flagons of foul local wine behind the stone pillars of those buildings that had been completed, the masked ceremonies on the stone floors with strange symbols, incantations, powders and pastes, and the reports of strange beasts tramping the Elysian Fields,

144

were too much for the family. On the Marquess's death his executors were instructed to recover, by any means necessary, all copies of the book. They succeeded, but history does not record the lengths to which they were forced to go. All that remains are the rumours of bribery, blackmail, poison, knives and gunpowder. And the continual assertion, carried on the deep undercurrents of informed opinion, that one copy still survives – somewhere.

Yes, if the writer had made it behind the leather-backed door of Mr Haines's study, he might have walked over to his desk – a wide mahogany affair with a green leather rectangle set into the surface – where there are two shallow mesh baskets, one with 'IN' written on it, the other 'OUT'. The 'OUT' box is usually empty and the 'IN' overflowing. There is a magnificent view out of the window – which is wider than the desk – from here. You can see the whole of the lawn. With your nose pressed against the glass and your head turned to one side you can even see the path that runs along the side of the Hall. And anyone on it.

Most of the contents of Mr Haines's 'IN' tray are dull – bills, begging letters, take-away menus, copies of the local parish magazine, unanswered requests to open village fêtes, that kind of thing – but sticking out between the pages of an election leaflet from the local Tory MP is a signed photo of a former member of the Baader-Meinhof gang, who is now... something else.

As we close for today, let us pause for a moment to consider the life developing in front of us on the printed page. That slow unravelling, the drying of feathers, the stretching of limbs, the ever-faster pumping of blood.

Day Six

Another day in paradise.

It was a case of déja vu with Stevenson at breakfast. I was up at the window again, staring at the arch in the distance, trying to see through it, to the world beyond, when he appeared, just like yesterday, and started discussing the view. Today, though, he was talking about the church, just visible to our left where its steeple poked out from the trees.

'Did you ever hear about the last vicar of this particular tiny parish, sir?' he asked.

He knew perfectly well that I knew nothing about this place apart from what I had been told – most of it by him – since I arrived here.

'No, Stevenson,' I replied, 'but I'd like to.'

As he told his story, he, too, stared out towards the arch.

'Well, sir,' he said, 'the parish shrank and shrank over the years, due to what we might perhaps call the 'social cleansing' programme of the first two Earls, until it consisted merely of a handful of servants living in tied cottages on the estate. As they died off, they were not replaced and the cottages were left to go to wrack and ruin. There are only a couple left now, sir, one of which is hard by the church itself.'

After a moment of silence, Stevenson continued.

'And then there came a point when the only member of the parish outside the Earl's immediate family was the vicar himself. He was a kindly old man, insubstantial physically but with an inner strength and of estimable good cheer – there was always a smile on his moon-like face. He was possessed of that most admirable and indefinable characteristic – now sadly almost completely unknown in this philistine land of ours – grace.'

Stevenson paused again, as if he was considering this vanished aspect of the national character.

'This was in the thirties, sir,' he carried on, 'a dark era in our nation's history, as I am sure you are aware – depression, unemployment, fascism and appeasement. And then, of course, war. The third Earl was an unappetising chap – even more so, it must be said, than his predecessors, whose patriotism, at least, was never in doubt. His portrait has since been banished to the servants' quarters, sir, and can be seen, should you find such a prospect appealing, in the staff refectory behind the kitchens. A dark, windowless room not much beloved of the domestics.' His voice descended for a moment to a hoarse whisper. 'It is said that the Earl has a physical presence there.' A hand rose smoothly to his mouth, where its arrival coincided with the neat wrapping and swallowing of a parcel of liquid in his throat. 'That presence,' he said, 'is a constant reminder to us of the consequences of cowardice and betrayal. The vicar, sir – his name was Harry – was left with little to do other than to maintain the church and devote himself to the spiritual needs of the Earl's family. Which, of course, were many. The Earl had a brother with a passion for roulette, and a sister, Estelle, who, upon her return to the Hall after a period of exile, made the most of her engagement with the high life by feeding young men an expensive diet of game and champagne in order to fuel the sexual energy she proceeded to drain from them. The family also included a young solicitor, forced by the greed of those above him in the noble food chain to earn his own living, who wrote for Oswald Mosley's *British Union Quarterly*, and a flighty dowager with an obsessive interest in Otto Rahn's Nazi-funded search for the Holy Grail. There was all manner of wickedness abroad here in those febrile days, sir. On a Sunday, Harry's services in the church, accompanied by old Mrs Dangerfield on the organ, were delivered to a congregation consisting purely – if you will forgive the word – of these ne'er-do-wells. The arrangement was obviously unsatisfactory, but Harry believed that it was his duty to God to persevere in his ministrations to his flock of black sheep and to hope for its regeneration. The Earl, however, was of a different mind. The presence of a building, owned by the Church of England, on his estate, even if its vicar was attempting to pursue the tricky task of securing a path to heaven for his nearest and dearest, was one that he found irksome in the extreme. The church was hanging on to its existence by the slimmest of threads – the lifeline of a single, very old man. There were, I believe, a series of chats with Harry. The vicar was benign and cheerful throughout, while the Earl's treatment of the old gentleman degenerated rapidly. Harry, you see, despite his equanimity and peaceful demeanour, was no pushover. He was adamant that God's work in the depleted parish must continue. The view of the relevant diocese of the Church of England (informed, no doubt, by those higher up the ecclesiastical ladder) was that the spiritual wellbeing of the noble family was important both as an example to the local population and as a bulwark to the very spirit of England itself.

'One morning, old Harry arrived to find the door of the church off its hinges. Inside, a trail of mud and animal excrement led to the altar, where the remains of a dead goat, its throat slit, lay in a pool of blood that had dripped on to the stone floor, forming red rivulets around the bricks and soaking into the earth below.'

Stevenson paused to allow the image to soak into my mind.

'For poor old Harry that was too much,' he continued. 'He collapsed on to the floor and never got up again. And that collapse, in turn, did for poor old Mrs Dangerfield. The next day, after completing an impassioned performance of Bach's *Toccata and Fugue in B Minor*, she was found dead on the church floor below the instrument's loft, having apparently hurled herself from it in despair.

'Afterwards, in public, the Earl howled in outrage and swore vengeance on the perpetrators of the diabolical act. As a testament of his devotion to his old parish priest, he insisted that Harry be buried, not in his home town five miles away, but in the grounds of the church he had loved. Three weeks later Harry's grave was desecrated. And that was the end of the line for the Bishop. He ordered that the building be deconsecrated – and sold, at a knockdown price, to the Earl. Harry's remains were removed to his home town after all, and I am happy to be able to tell you, sir, that he rests in peace there to this day. There were rumours in later weeks and months of further devilish activity in the church and churchyard. Confirmation, you see, that the Church had been right to remove itself from the estate. The decision to do so had attracted some opprobrium in certain quarters but the view that this was a matter best shoved out of sight and forgotten, prevailed. It was maintained that old Mrs Dangerfield's ghost returned to play the organ at midnight every Saturday. There was talk of red-eyed, horned creatures gambolling amongst the gravestones. Peasant talk – you know how it is, sir.'

Stevenson had turned to look at me.

'The product of ill-educated minds and superstition. Our society's pagan roots. A strange brew concocted of ancient customs and local liquors. Which brings us to today, sir,' he concluded brightly. 'Would you care to be outside, on the steps, any time between nine thirty and ten? I hope that the day will prove to be as interesting as any that have gone before.'

As he turned and began to move silently towards the kitchen, arms parallel with his sides, feet barely lifting from the floor, Catherine took his place, a coffee mug in her hand. She was wearing a mauve sweater and blue jeans. There was blusher on her cheeks, her lips were red, and the brightness of her eyes was reflected in diamond earrings. Thick, shining dark hair fell over the polo-neck of her jumper. She was smiling as she watched Stevenson glide across the floor.

'He's a wonder, isn't he?' she said. She was posher now, away from the actors.

'He's an interesting guy,' I said. 'I'm learning a lot from him. Although some of it may be total bollocks.'

She laughed and turned to look at me. Fast-flowing blood.

Filled with vitamins and oxygen.

'Do you know what's happening today?' she asked.

'No,' I said, 'but if we're going chronologically then I can guess.'

'You must know a lot about Luke,' she said.

'I'm starting to,' I said. 'Were you a fan of his – before you met him?'

'What an interesting question,' she replied, finishing her coffee and dabbing her mouth with a neatly folded white handkerchief. Then she looked at her watch.

'Oh dear, surely that can't be right, can it? I must go,' she said. 'It's so hard to fit everything in to the day, isn't it? I am sorry. See you soon.'

Down at the far end of the room the actors' table was deserted and Mary was clearing it away, scraping cornflakes and bits of toast into a dish on her trolley.

'I like what you're doing,' I said after Catherine. 'The acting.'

'See you tomorrow,' she said over one shoulder as she left.

Tomorrow? Odd that she had chosen a day when I'd hardly see her to introduce herself.

At 9.45 I walked through the main door of the Hall out on to the steps at the north entrance. The sky seemed wider than ever – as if extra air had been puffed into it in the night. Stevenson was already there. It looked as though he'd been there a while, actually, but he didn't seem bothered. He was standing to attention by the Daimler. He smiled as I went down the steps towards him.

'Let us go and pay another of our visits, sir, shall we? Who knows what we will find today?'

I climbed in and off we went.

We went the same way as the day before. This time, though, we drove straight past the wrecked car – no bloodstained bodies today – and before long were heading across the field towards the gate. I repeated my helping hand bit there and then we carried on again, the other side of the road, into the wood. And then we were out of the trees and pulling up once more in front of the semis.

When we got out today, though, it was the second house, the one on the left, that we walked towards. Stevenson took out his keys and opened the door. There was a dark chest of drawers in the hallway, on a carpet of dark-flecked light blue. The kitchen door ahead was closed. From upstairs we could hear the sound of someone picking on an acoustic guitar. Stevenson led the way up.

At the top of the staircase we turned left, towards the smaller of the two bedrooms at the front of the house. On the other side of the dividing wall was the room where we had heard Catherine talking about Joe. The door was open. The curtains were closed and it was dark, but there was a bell-shaped blur of light around a shaded table-lamp by the dishevelled bed. The actor who looked like Haines was sitting there, trying to pick out a tune. He didn't look up as we went in. We stood at the back of the room and watched him as, head down, he tried different sections of the song. It was 'Some Changes' from the Auteurs album *How I Learned to Love the Bootboys*. Then he lifted his head and sang it. He managed the mixture of half-snarls and strange pathos pretty well – it could almost have been Haines himself over there. The song's about ignoring the past and living for the present – and the future. He sang while staring at the wall above our heads, the bell-bottom of his jeans flapping as a dirty trainer kept time on a floor covered in discarded clothes. For one line, though, his eyes flicked downwards. It's about Haines receiving a death threat – a note saying that he's 'scum' and he's going to die. He flung that one directly at me.

When he had finished he squeezed past us with his guitar, banging it on the door frame. As he moved along the landing, we heard him pummel the instrument's body, and the sound, amplified by the wood and air, echoed around the ceiling as he made his way downstairs. I looked at Stevenson, expecting a signal for us to move on, but he didn't budge. Something caught my eye. I looked back at the bed. From the jumble of duvet, sheets and blankets an arm, then a head, then a torso were emerging. It was a kid – the Kid, the Killer's sidekick.

He had been lying there in that jumble of bedclothes behind the actor all the time. He looked a mess. An unappetising smell briefly wafted over us, but Stevenson gave no sign of having noticed it.

The Kid had a transistor radio in his hand, which was playing very quietly – the song was 'Jukebox Jive' by the Rubettes. He put it down on a table beside the bed and switched it off. Then he turned the light off, too, and settled back down beneath the covers. Through the gloom we could just make out small, regular movements beneath the bedclothes. I looked at Stevenson. He flicked his head towards the door.

I stood on the landing, looking over the banisters to the hall below. There was a low murmur of conversation coming from somewhere down there. Stevenson passed behind me and led the way down.

There was a comforting solidity about this pair of houses. The carpets were thick, and sound disappeared into them. From the style, they would have been built in the thirties. Long enough ago for them to have bedded down, but not to have been given anything as dangerous as a history.

The conversation Stevenson and I heard on the way down the stairs was different to anything we had heard over the last few days. A man and a woman were talking but their tones of voice and their formality marked their relationship out as something from a more paternalistic, tighter-lipped era.

We walked in to the lounge.

The cream curtains at the bay window were drawn and they hung down in perfect vertical pleats, ending at the point where the carpet began. The room was bright, though – it was well-lit by a chandelier-effect central light and a white standard lamp topped with a shade the shape of a pillbox hat. The brown three-piece suite had thin cushions and hard backs, wooden arm-rests, and legs like those of a sleek fifties housewife in tan stockings and heels. In the sealed fireplace there was a 'real-look coal fire', its false flames rippling upwards mechanically, and abjectly failing to conjure up any ghosts of coal-dust, ash or charcoal. Above the fireplace, in the middle of some ripple-effect white wallpaper, was an oil painting of a fishing village, with a small boat hauled up on to the beach in the foreground.

In front of the fireplace, on one of the armchairs, sat the younger actor, the one who had played James and Jim, but looking now as if he was in early middle-age. He was wearing a pair of National Health glasses, and his short, dark hair was neatly parted at the side and combed across his head. He had a short-sleeved grey jumper over a white shirt that was clasped at each elbow by an elasticated silver band. Neatly knotted inside the 'V' of the jumper was what could have been an old school tie. His legs were crossed and his hands clasped in his lap on top of a newspaper. Sitting opposite him, on a sofa underneath an oil painting of a cathedral, was a woman whose hair was lighter, longer and curlier than his, but parted and dragged in the same way. It was the second actress. She wore a grey pencil skirt, into which a thin cashmere sweater was trimly tucked. Round her neck was a pearl necklace, and her sleeves were pushed up to her elbows. She wore pale pink lipstick.

Stevenson and I were standing just inside the door.

The couple were husband and wife – nothing in the world could be as obvious as that. Their conversation had stopped abruptly as soon as we appeared and they were looking at us with a mixture of discomfort and mild annoyance. That only lasted a few seconds, though. Then they turned back to each other again and continued their discussion. This seemed to give Stevenson permission for us to walk in. He stepped on to the crimson carpet, and then across a large, broadly patterned rug in red and green, towards the second armchair, next to the husband's. I was left with the sofa, where I sat a polite distance from the wife.

'I really think it's the right time,' she was saying. 'I'm not getting any younger.'

Her husband demurred:

'You don't look a day over twenty, my dear.'

She smiled.

'Thank you, Henry,' she said, 'but the clock is ticking, you know.'

153

He looked bemused.

'The biological clock,' she said.

'Ah,' he said, but looked little the wiser.

'Well you know what they're all telling us now,' he said. 'Life begins at forty.'

The newspaper had slipped slightly on his lap and I could see an odd Gothic masthead saying *The Daily Telegraph*.

'That may be so,' she said, 'but I think it's time for us to start a family. We women know about these things, you know.'

That seemed to defeat her husband.

'Yes, of course,' he said, adding as a final shot: 'Well, we'll have to pull in our horns.'

'You've always been good with money,' she said. 'You've always looked after me.'

He smiled at that.

'We'll be all right, dear,' he said.

And then it was her turn to smile.

'You'll be doing your antenatal classes with lots of strange-looking girls in short skirts and flowery hair, you know.'

'You could be there, too. You could come with me. There'll be lots of young men. There are these days.'

He looked bemused by the prospect.

'I don't think so,' he said and paused. Then he said again, 'I don't think so.'

'Oh, I didn't tell you,' his wife said. 'Marjorie and Hugh have invited us for dinner.'

'Oh, wonderful,' said her husband, his face brightening. 'It's been ages since I saw Hugh. We'll be able to have a good chat.'

'And Margaret wants me to help with the flowers for Harvest Festival.'

'Marvellous,' he replied. 'The two of you will do a grand job.'

They sat in silence for a moment and then the husband said:

'What's for supper, darling?'

'It's your favourite,' she replied. 'Lamb chops. With mint sauce and boiled potatoes.'

'Terrific,' he said. 'Need a hand with the spuds?'

'That would be nice,' she replied.

With that, they both got up and the husband followed his wife into the kitchen.

Once they had gone, Stevenson stood up and went over to the curtains, which he opened. Then he went over to the fire, which he turned off – then he did the same for all the lights. As soon as he had sat down again, the husband came back in. He had removed the sleeveless sweater, but otherwise looked the same.

He walked over to the huge, square television set and turned it on. It stood on four metal legs and had two large dials below its screen, set into a yellow and black grille. It wasn't until he had sat down again that a picture appeared there – in black and white. There were dancers gyrating – girls in hooped minidresses and boots, tiny skirts and crocheted tops, and blokes in suede jackets and drainpipes, ruched white shirts and flares. The band behind them was Procol Harum and the song was 'A Whiter Shade of Pale'. The husband sighed, got up from his chair and grappled with one of the saucer-like dials on the front of the television set. Greeted by the sight of a chimpanzee in a tree, he snorted and turned it off.

Settling back in his chair, he addressed us.

'My wife's having a baby,' he said. 'In the autumn. It's going to mean some changes.' He pondered this for a moment and then went on. 'I suppose it's the right time. By the time the little blighter grows up, all this' – he waved a hand at the television – 'will be over. Flash in the pan. Not British at all. One ruined generation will be enough to show society the error of its ways. Some sanity will have returned to the world by then. A man will know where he is again. The boy will have a chance to make something of himself.'

'We've done all right, the wife and I,' he continued. 'Made a good life. Enjoyed ourselves together. We've got some good memories. Wonderful times. We're settled, it's time to look to the future. We should count our blessings – we survived the war and we survived the peace. And now we're thriving. Wonderful times.' He paused for a moment, looking down at his lap. And then he lifted his head again. 'This is our summer. I've worked hard and so has the wife, bless her, keeping the house spick and span and working wonders in the kitchen. Of course, some of the people we knew never made it this far. Thanks to Hitler. Uncle Bob. Mr Spellthorne. The grocer's son, Kenneth, lost a leg. And Kenneth's cousin was blinded by a tracer bullet.' Suddenly he brightened. 'I know! Let's have some proper music, shall we?'

He went over to a wooden storage unit with sliding doors that stood on the floor behind the TV. Opening it, he stood for a minute crouching in front of it, and then took out a record. Then he walked over to the corner by the window, where there was a small mono record player. Lifting up the top, he put the album on to the turntable. Then he pulled back the white plastic arm until it clicked and carefully lowered its hooked head until the concealed needle bit on the vinyl. After a short burst of crackling, we heard the strings of an orchestra swell stridently from the tiny speaker at the front. He put the lid down again and immediately the sound lost its rough edge. The mellow voice of Perry Como began to croon 'Catch a Falling Star'. As the husband settled back in his chair, Stevenson lifted his eyebrows and tilted his head towards the door. We left him to his music. Back in the hall, Stevenson said, 'How about a little fresh air, sir?', and off we went, through the kitchen, into the back garden.

The garden was made up of a succession of three squares – upper lawn, rockery, lower lawn – all beautifully maintained, with the edges of the flower beds perfectly straight and the brightly coloured flowers separated by moist soil that was uncontaminated by weeds. We crossed the first section of lawn and then took the footpath that circled the rockery. There was some kind of water-effect oozing clear liquid over the stones and making a happy gurgling sound.

As we reached the bottom lawn, the fence that separated this garden from the one next door became a low hedge. On the other side of it there was a croquet lawn. There were white hoops sticking out like giant paper clips, and multi-coloured balls punctuating the green grass.

There was a narrow gap in the hedge halfway down and Stevenson surprised me by walking through it. I followed him. At the bottom of the other garden was a small thicket with a path leading through it. We took the path, brushed a few pine branches away from our faces and found ourselves in front of a large, windowless summer house. There was a heavy padlock on the door. Stevenson took out his keys again and opened it. We stepped inside.

It was dark in there. There was a smell of wood varnish and a hint of sawdust. I couldn't make out much in the gloom, just a series of what looked like long display units, like you get in a museum. Stevenson flicked on the light – and immediately everything got a lot clearer.

All round the walls of the summer house there were banners, flags, pennants and framed photographs, posters and certificates. The flags were swastikas, the banners and pennants belonged to the Afrika Korps, Hitler Youth and Waffen-SS. As I walked along the walls I saw photographs of Hitler, Himmler, Goering, Rommel and plenty more I didn't recognise, all in Nazi uniform. There were signatures on a couple. Everything was neatly hung and equally spaced.

I started walking round the display cases. There were Lugers, Iron Crosses, hip flasks, stiletto knives, cigarette cases, pill boxes, magazine clips, holsters on thin black belts, silver spurs, field glasses. You could picture the Nazi leaders, decked out in this stuff, standing on the French coast looking across at the white cliffs and smiling. One cabinet had a collection of worn leather writing cases, each open on a letter written in German. I had a look at a few of them, but I couldn't understand anything much. My German's almost non-existent, but I know what 'Meine liebe' means – a lot of them began like that.

There were mannequins wearing Nazi and Gestapo uniforms. Peaked hats and eagles, silver and black. The devil gets the best uniforms. The blank faces of the dummies toned down the effect, though. You needed the expression of a human being there to fully appreciate it.

At the back of the hut was a cylindrical stand, metal-shelved and packed with handguns. You could turn it round and examine everything there, like a shopper considering a purchase. I started to feel very cold, surrounded by all these things – weapons that had actually killed, uniforms that had been worn by murderers.

Stevenson was at the front of the hut, looking down the channel between the display cases towards me. I walked back up to him.

'It is not a pleasant sight, sir, is it?' he said as I got closer, his words bouncing off the glass cases.

'I don't understand it, Stevenson,' I said. 'Here in England…'

'My father told me once,' he said, 'that evil looks for a warm place in which to settle. He recalled to me some of the things he had heard from the lips of noble Englishmen in the thirties – at a time, sir, when the threat from Hitler and his henchmen was already very clear. Words, spoken in an easy confidence amongst friends – and in front of servants. Two groups of people who could be relied upon to be discrete. The one complicit, the other loyal. My father only spoke years afterwards about what he had heard there. And even then, I believe – for that is what he said – only to me. And that was in the course of a lesson about the very quality of loyalty. He believed that his employers, with the benefit of their expensive educations and their God-given position, were superior to him. That their beliefs and decisions were necessarily correct. That his own views, if contradictory to theirs, would perforce be wrong. That, for instance, even if every fibre of his being was straining in support of the conviction that a man's love of his country's freedom countermanded his sense of duty to a personal friend who threatened that freedom – then he must be mistaken. Needless to say, sir, I have grown up with a very different definition of the word 'loyalty'. When the opportunity came to test my father's assertion – when I had friends who, shall we say, espoused the cause of 'the people' – I had no misgivings about my summary rejection of them.'

He turned.

'I think I hear footsteps,' he said. 'We may be about to find out more about the owner of this distressing collection.'

We turned to face the door. There was a man standing there. He was wearing a sharp dark suit, with a silver pin just below the knot of his royal blue tie. It was the actor who had played Joe.

'Good day, gentlemen,' he said. 'I see that you are interested in my collection. Let me satisfy your curiosity. But I think we should go outside. You may have preconceptions that need to be blown away by a breath of fresh English air.'

We followed him back out, through the tightly packed trees and on to his croquet lawn. The healthy green of the grass and the bright colours of the flowers at the top of the garden were a welcome sign of normality after the contents of that place. Nearer the house there were three white chairs arranged around a white garden table. We followed him there. Stevenson was impassive but for the first time I got the impression that he was not particularly happy about his attendance at one of our sessions.

'You see,' said the man, 'I was born in this country.'

He looked at each of us in turn, as if challenging us. He must have guessed that we were born here, too. That we would have an equal stake in what he was about to say.

'I was born here,' he repeated, 'and I will die here. In England. In the Home Counties. But before that happens I want certain things to happen. And they will. Margaret Thatcher never understood us. A grocer's daughter from Lincolnshire – she thought she could represent us. She wanted to be one of us but she tried to bring us down to her level. She kept looking for the lowest common denominator. We are made of more intellectual, more moral stuff. She courted the pornographic tabloid press. She argued with the royal family. She compared herself to Winston Churchill, the war criminal. She's gone now. Gone and forgotten. And we will rebuild what she destroyed – class, religion, culture. We will have a new leader.' He crossed his legs, took out a pipe and began to stuff it with tobacco. 'My father died in 1953. The year the king died. The year his queen became the queen mother. My father has returned to me recently – I have conversed with his spirit. It was a success. I saw what I wanted to see and heard what I wanted to hear. My old father spoke of the future. I returned here a new man.'

He pondered this for a moment. The pipe was on the table, unlit. Next to it, there was a jug of iced tea. He poured himself a glass and offered us one. We declined.

'The gods have smiled on us,' he said. 'A new day is dawning. We will have ourselves a new leader – and what if he is an old man? He will be reborn. He will have the old charisma, the old magic.'

He laughed warmly.

'We'll welcome him. We'll stand there, awestruck. In suits and ties, with our hair cut short. Our ladies in long dresses and pearls and sculptured hair. Children's faces filled with unearthly joy. Mothers' cheeks will bloom. Fathers' eyes grow bright... I was born here and I will die here. England is mine. England made me. Listen to me. Heed what I say. We are angry and we are coming closer. We will swell in your eyes as we move toward you from your horizon. Our time is coming. We have all been reborn. We are new men. Soon my job will be done. I will be able to rest easy. On England's soil. I was born here and I will die here.' Suddenly he went very quiet. 'My little girl,' he said, 'she doesn't speak to me.'

He wrenched his tie and top button loose with that final sentence. Then his head sank on to his chest.

Stevenson was easing himself up from his chair. Once he was clear of it, I did the same. We walked back over to the hedge. I turned back to look at the man. He hadn't moved but his pipe had fallen on to the ground.

As we walked back up the garden on the other side of the fence Stevenson had his hands clasped behind his back. He was grimacing.

'An unappetising creature,' he said. 'Confused, sentimental and sick. A smalltown apocalyptic neo-fascist.'

'Well, it takes all sorts,' I laughed, trying to cheer him up.

Stevenson looked across at me.

'I am not sure that evil should be regarded merely as a quaint personality trait, sir.'

'Yes. You're right, of course, Stevenson,' I said. 'I apologise.'

'Oh, no need for that, sir. I think you are as relieved to get away from that macabre museum and its mad master as I am myself. You were just letting your exuberance run away with you a little. We need to remember, though, that nostalgia and fascism are two sides of the same coin. If today teaches us anything perhaps it will be that.'

We were back in the house. Stevenson had wiped his shoes meticulously on the doormat. We were going upstairs again. On the way, I had a quick look through the door of the lounge. The husband was there in front of the television, watching *The Val Doonican Show*.

Back upstairs we returned to the bedroom where we had seen the performance of 'Some Changes'. Fortunately the Kid had gone. The actor who had played Haines was back, though, and this time he was standing in front of a full-length mirror, a comb in one hand. He was wearing a pair of blue cords and a red shirt. I could see his face reflected in the mirror as he spoke.

'Oxford bags. Loon pants. Denim jackets and cheesecloth shirts,' he said. 'Disco at the church hall. See the girls dancing. See the glitter on their cheeks. Stand by the wall and watch. When you go out, the bootboys are hanging out, waiting to pick on you. Don't use their nicknames, 'cos then you're just playing their game. Call them John and Andrew and Michael. Turn them back into kids. Talk to them. Pretend you like them. Pretend you think they're smart. They don't know what I want. But with my brains and their brawn we could really get somewhere. John, Andrew, Michael.'

He dragged the comb through his hair again.

'Malcolm, the old teddy boy, the failed revolutionary,' he said. 'When he got the Pistols together, he was trying to bring back 1955. He wanted his black and white telly back. There's nothing worse than a sentimental red provocateur. England in the pissing rain – it's no setting for a revolution, is it? But it's enough to turn you to devil worship and suicide instead – GPO, comprehensive schools, British Leyland. The French do these things so much better. Even if they can't play rock and roll. Keep smoking the continental cigarettes, Malcolm –

161

Situationists beat Seditionaries every time. But always take a genuine Auteur over one of them. Born in the seventies. Glam rock, punk rock, Auteurs. Next in line. The next batch of kids are opening their infant eyes, sensing each other's presence.'

Then he turned round to face us. He took a chair from a desk by the wall, pulled it into the middle and sat down.

'I'm waiting for a man – well, one thing is as good as another. We'll go past the bridge where the suicide kids jump. He knows all the best places. Past the precinct, past the kids hanging round the flats – the mums and dads inside, with their booze and their fags and their tellies. Your uncle's flat, third floor, fourth door along, plant pot and windowbox. "Sit on me, boy."'

He leaned towards me.

'He told me a story, your uncle. I'll tell it to you.'

When he spoke again, his voice was deeper and he spoke slowly. He had become an Essex man, an estuary man, with a rasp in his voice. A sixty a day man. He wasn't looking at us any more – he was looking past us, out of the window, into the sky.

'You have to grow into this, you know, it doesn't come out of nothing... And practice makes perfect. He was a good kid. No complaints from him so none from me. He can come back any time. My arm round his neck. His red skin. Then my hands round his neck, fingers on the windpipe – there's nothing to beat it. And now he's lying there all nice and still. All ready to go. Back to the water. Proper little martyr. They want to die – you're doing them a favour. They want the tabloid headlines when they're dead. It's what they live for. I downed a few beers and then we got going – he'd been very patient. He's a good kid. I dumped him in the river. Piss-stained Y-fronts, a trail down his white legs. My hands under his legs. Sticky legs.'

He held his gaze silently for a moment and then closed his eyes.

Then he straightened again and opened his eyes slowly.

'Dead of night,' he said quietly, the Essex man gone. 'Shouts and screams and bottles smashing. Laughter and heels scraping on gravel. A door slamming. And then quiet. Here he comes. Grey in the black night. Money is exchanged. And then you drive. And you drive. For long enough to forget who you are. Out to the woods – deep in the woods. The girl asleep in the back. Tonight all the lights are out. The country has run out of power. The country has run out of energy. Britain has fallen asleep. It's a nation united in darkness. Let it wrap itself around her. Get out slowly. Pick her up gently, carry her in your arms. Fold her dress neatly underneath her. Take her over there and put her under the trees. Deep under. Cover her up. Nice and warm. She's still asleep. So tired.' He stared at me. 'Maybe she's dreaming of you?'

He leaned back again. Then he shook his head. Standing up, he pushed the chair away and turned to face the mirror again. Taking out his comb once more, he resumed the careful sifting of his hair.

I don't know if there was a lunch bell today. I never heard one.

It was just me at supper. No Stevenson – Mary served me. She barely spoke: 'Yes, sir', 'No, sir', 'I don't know, sir', 'Will that be all, sir?' When I asked her if she had seen Stevenson, she didn't reply.

Editor's note—

Ah – the actor who looks like Mr Haines takes centre stage. Blue cords and a red shirt – dear me. There will need to be some changes there. Through his lips we hear stories of murder. And the Auteurs begin to rise up through his mind and out through his body on to the drive of an English suburban home.

Mr Haines had been working on the *How I Learned to Love the Bootboys* record, on which today's performances are based, at around the same time as *England Made Me*. However, it was not released until 1999. At one point it had been scheduled to come out first. That would have made more sense as it is an Auteurs album – the last Auteurs album, in fact. By now Mr

Haines was barely visible within the world of rock and roll. More than ever, he was out on his own. Up in the sky. The *Bootboys* album was originally due to be released on May 31st – the day in the ancient calendar when the old god was killed to make way for the new.

Mr Haines believes in what he terms 'hostalgia'. The anti-nostalgia. The picture of the black-eyed boy on the cover of *Now I'm a Cowboy* is an early example. It is wrong to look at the past through rose-coloured spectacles – that tint, after all, may come from blood diluted with tears. No – one should live only in the present and the future. Where there is life. The past is to move on from.

The song 'Some Changes' is defined by its hostalgic bile. There is a line about the way we remember the weather when we were young – about how the summers were always hotter when we were children and it always snowed at Christmas. Mr Haines had recently been interviewed by a young whippersnapper who produced an Auteurs fanzine. There is a line in the song about a youngster telling the narrator that he needs to raise his game. Perhaps the cheeky little pipsqueak had made an impact on the great man!

It would have been interesting to have found out more about the husband and wife. They are obviously not 'Luke Haines''s parents, but their circumstances seem to be similar to those of the husband and wife in Mr Haines's autobiographical *Bootboys* song, '1967'. Perhaps they are friends or neighbours making guest appearances? I believe that there were various objects in the front room (a couple of magazines on the bottom of a pile on the table, a cardboard box on a shelf etc.) which, if the writer had been more observant, might have given him more of an idea of where they were 'coming from'. Inside the cardboard box, for instance, are photographic memories of the spring of the husband's relationship with his wife. In *Seance on a Wet Afternoon*, Myra has a biscuit tin in which she collects money from the clients attending her séances. The photos in the husband's box are nostalgic, but the coins in Myra's tin are hostalgic – they are directly related to the unpaid 'performances' of her psychic art which she was forced to give as a child. Myra knows that she must move on from the minor acclaim and pale love of her petty customers and finally convert her child-stardom into the real thing. She must become an occult celebrity.

The 'neo-fascist next door' – there's one in every street, isn't there? A more careful examination of some of the exhibits in his museum would have revealed more. But then I suppose that would have necessitated a knowledge of the German language a little wider than one capable merely of translating the word 'liebe'. Education, education, education.

Stevenson's remarks about nostalgia and fascism remind me of the sleeve of the Auteurs' single 'The Rubettes'. It features a tableau of a masked man in a splashsuit and rubber gloves, being watched by a child in a pink blanket. The man in the suit seems to be about to commit a messy murder. There is a truck – possibly a cattle truck – with an old couple inside. There are also barbed wire fences. We must always be ready for the past to return in disguise.

In Mr Haines's song 'Lights Out', set amidst the dark night of the three-day week, a man drives a young woman out to the woods to meet her end. He remarks that her guardian angel can no longer see her. He is right. The angel concerned is lost. He is up in the sky, stumbling around in the gloom, blind. The woman will die. In *Seance on a Wet Afternoon*, Myra tells the kidnapped girl that her own guardian angel has put candles on both her knees – white on the left, blue on the right – to protect her. Myra is merely trying to calm the young girl – she does not really believe that the angel will protect her. But what she says is true. The angel has flown down with the candles and is watching the girl by their light. She will live. Myra's psychic power has been shown to be less than that of a common murderer. Myra tells Billy to kill the girl they have kidnapped. But Billy disobeys Myra. Instead he puts her gently down on a bed of leaves underneath a tree. He leaves her where she will be found.

But maybe the real Billy would have killed her. For this is not the real Billy. Billy was played by Richard Attenborough – the gang leader Pinky in *Brighton Rock*, the murderer Christie in *10 Rillington Place*. Attenborough, though, was sick on the day this scene was shot, gripped by pain from stones that had formed inside him, and dosed up with morphine. And so it is not the real Billy who saves the girl from Myra. It is the film's director, Bryan Forbes, who puts on the helmet and goggles. He disguises himself as the already disguised kidnapper. It is Forbes, not Attenborough, who three times emerges from the fog and staggers towards the camera. It is Forbes who leaves the girl for the scouts to find. The real Billy has been sedated. The real Billy has slept through it all. This scene was shot in Forbes's garden. The woods in his Murder Park were his woods – and there was to be no murder. The girl was found by the scout leader. The scout leader was played by Eddie, Mr Forbes's gardener.

The writer misses out on lunch of his own volition today – the bell was indeed sounded. I do believe that what he is hearing and seeing is starting to interfere with his appetite. Or his sense of hearing. Or his sense of reality. It is not often that one sees the visceral effect of art on an audience. I am pleased with the way that Mr Haines's tying-together of his personal life with the reality of seventies provincial England, against a background of our national history, has shown the capacity for evil in all of us – even the best – and has obviously brought it home in a very deep way to this particular audience member.

At the end of today's section of the writer's catalogue of misfortune there came a rather bizarre departure. The writer printed the text of an email which he claimed to have recently received – but of the email itself, or of an original message from the writer to which it is allegedly a response, I can find no trace. Perhaps, though, the email does exist somewhere. The purported sender is a person dwelling in some kind of post-Baader-Meinhof netherworld. But perhaps this person is actually some kind of prankster? Or is it, perhaps, the case – this is just an idea – that the message which the writer 'quotes' is merely another example of his wandering imagination, and further evidence of his deepening mental malaise?

This is how the email reads:

'Guten tag! Greetings from what will, I hope, one day be the truly Democratic Republic of Germany. I have read your message and will now help you in your project. I am unsure if Luke will be happy that I am talking to you so maybe it is better if you keep your silence with him on this subject. If you are talking with him at all. You did not make this clear in your message. Luke and I spent much time together at the dawn of the millennium. As you may know he was much excited with the possibility of recording a sequel to his artistically complete but commercially void album about our famous terrorists the RAF. I have many good memories of this time but you may find that Luke has different memories. Or, more likely, that he prefers to remember these times differently. The revolutionary struggle will succeed through such contradictions. I introduced Luke to some interesting people, but they will not thank me for bringing their names into the light and so it is better that the identities of those with revolutionary thoughts remain secret. Their words, however, will bring the day of change closer and must be heard. I will repeat some of these words to you without names and you will publish them in your book. Luke and I had some fun times here in Berlin. With our vodka and our aspirin and our night driving. I have some good stories I can tell you. Maybe later. I should first be in the right mood. You will write to me some questions and I will examine them and reply as I wish. Some of your questions I will not reply to – this is how it must be. You will respond soon, I think.

Klaus Wolf.'

Right, in search of the kind of enlightenment that we have not received from the writer, we now return to my encounter with Mr Haines. Let us hear more of his words of wisdom!

At this point, I recall, my host had been interrupted by a call from Stevenson regarding the sudden unavailability for supper that night of the porker that Mr Haines had been eyeing – apparently the chunky chap had made an unexpected bid for freedom and was being hunted through the woods by the aged gardeners armed with their pitchforks. Mr Haines took the news in his stride and magnanimously agreed to devour a plump Viennese goose instead. Once he was settled again, I proceeded.

Why, I wondered, had he forsaken his previous distance from his own background and written autobiographically for the *Bootboys* album?'

He raised an eyebrow at me.

'After *Baader Meinhof*,' he said, 'which was a mixture of reportage and biography, and *England Made Me* – character-driven vignettes – it was a light relief to write autobiographically. That was partly why the ESP thing got ditched. I wouldn't go to my own records – or anywhere else – for self-help.'

This seemed to be an appropriate moment to don my arm-chair psychiatrist's hat.

'How much of your father do you see in yourself?' I asked, leaning slightly towards my subject. 'Do you think you will become more like him as you get older?'

Mr Haines inflated his cheeks – and then exhaled noisily.

'Not much. Although his natural bent is artistic it was never fully realised and just became assimilated. I am probably more likely to see myself becoming more like him in the next few years.'

'And what do your parents think about your songs?'

'It's all just music to them. They like the ones with nice tunes.'

'What kind of music did they listen to when you were growing up?'

'"Little Green Apples' by Roger Miller was played a lot. That and a bit of Frank.'

I removed my hat and leant backwards again. What of Mr Haines's life outside the family household, I was wondering? How did he fit into the landscape in which he found himself?

'Were you free to roam around your neighbourhood when you were a young lad?' I asked.

'On the days when I didn't attend school, I would wander through the fields behind our house for hours.'

'Ah,' I replied. 'Something tells me you may have taken leave of absence from your studies on a regular basis?'

Mr Haines remained straight-faced.

'The best thing I did as a kid,' he said, 'was to feign a neurological illness for three months in order to get me out of going to school. I was ten. I'd sussed out that school was mainly a brain-numbing grind and my time could be better spent lolling around at home watching reruns of *Jason King*, *The Protectors* and old war films.'

'Was there anything about school that you enjoyed?' I asked. Raffia perhaps, or cheering from the sidelines during football matches – maybe toad in the hole on Thursdays?

'No,' he responded. 'I resented spending my time with – mainly – retards. Teachers and pupils.'

'Did you play any sport?'

'Only when I had to.'

I pressed home my advantage.

'Did you ever get into trouble with the authorities?'

'Nothing major. I knew there was nothing to be gained. Minor acts of subversion were fun. Deliberately scoring an own goal in football. Catching a teacher out in cricket...'

The major acts were obviously to be saved for later. I narrowed my eyes.

'You have kindly revealed to me the best thing that happened to you as a nipper. What was the worst?'

Mr Haines looked me full in the face. Our gazes met. As my eyes were half-closed he was probably able to see more of me than I of him.

'The awful worry my 'illness' caused my parents,' he replied. 'But when you have a plan you have to see it through to the bitter end.'

He paused again and licked his lips. Then he carried on.

'After many hospital examinations, where nothing was found to be wrong with me, it was decreed that I was just a delicate child who was probably being bullied. It was therefore decided that I would attend school part-time to reintegrate me. I'd had my fun, so I knuckled under.'

'Was there much bullying at your school?'

'Most certainly,' he acknowledged, 'but actually it didn't affect me, really. If the occcasion did arise that the local tough nuts were on your case it did at least break the tedium of the

English comprehensive school system.'

He coughed theatrically, juggling the phlegm in his throat.

'Did you get into any rough and tumble with the local likely lads?' I asked.

'No. The tough kids all liked me. I wasn't perceived as a threat. I could also make them laugh. A cliché, I know. I found that if you ignored their hard-nut nicknames and addressed them by their first names this usually pacified them.'

'And what kinds of gangs were there in your vicinity at this time, sir?'

He brushed a hand disdainfully against his thigh.

'Well, this was the early eighties. It was the time of the second or third skinhead revival, all the crap TwoTone bands provided a turd for the flies to feast on. Nothing really changes. Kids will always test the boundaries, even if this means carrying knives or throwing acid over each other.'

Quite. Well, we have the knives – will the acid be next?

'Was the desire for revenge a part of your adolescence?' I enquired.

'It's there from my childhood,' he replied briskly, 'as early as I can remember. I am not an American, so I have not been in therapy. I know and care not for the reasons why. I am very happy about it.'

I reached behind me again for that psychoanalytical hat.

'Did you have much conflict with your parents when you were growing up?'

'The only real conflict was that my parents, who were relatively old when they had me, didn't really have any reference point for what I wanted to do. Music was something you danced to – in a dance hall or a ballroom. Art was Van Gogh, Monet etc. There were no sub-groups. They were both in their early thirties by the time of the first Beatles LP.' He sighed. 'All this is getting very Larkin, I know. Consequently all that modern age stuff passed them by. All of which is for the best, and I wouldn't change it at all.'

'Did you have any feelings of paranoia when you were growing up?' I asked.

'No, I didn't drink then,' he responded quickly.

'Manic/depressive behaviour patterns?'

'No, I am not depressive and I certainly don't bottle it up. I know that manic/depressives get a lot done on the up swing so you have to look on the positive side. I suffered from OCD in my early teens, but cured myself.'

This was interesting. What was the cure, one wonders? – to oneself. For it is not right to pry into such intimate details of a gentleman's life. Perhaps, though, it would have been achieved by a programme of electric shocks, ice baths and prolonged celibacy?

We have the man. In the brief time we have left we must find out more about the boy. Mr Haines was beginning to show signs of impatience with my questioning. A facial twitch, a glance towards the window, a drawing in of the foot across the carpet. Nothing major. Nothing impolite.

'Did you live in your imagination as a youngster?' I asked.

'Possibly. But I kept my eyes open and took it all in.'

'Were you self-confident?'

'I don't remember lacking confidence particularly. Pre-teen, people said I was shy. I think I was just reserved. As I am now.'

He yawned.

Just a couple more questions, sir, if you please.

Had Mr Haines's childhood been the best time of his life, I wondered? – until his recent good fortune, of course.

'Childhood was a drag,' he said.

'What methods did you employ to survive its longueurs?'

'When I appear to be doing nothing I am actually plotting.'

A useful point on which to conclude the interview.

Thank you, Mr Haines, for your gracious submission to this grilling.

Day Seven

How much longer is this going to go on?

It can't be more than a few days. And then I'll walk back up the drive to a waiting taxi and it'll return me to the station. And then I'll go home. Back to the real world. My room, the city, the noise and the dirt, all those people – the magazine. And all this down here will carry on without me. A few strange people playing games.

I spoke to Catherine again at breakfast. She joined me as I was refilling my coffee cup.

'What was yesterday like?' she asked, standing close.

'It was fine,' I said. 'But there was something missing.'

'Oh, what was that?' she asked, leaning against the table, her skirt tightening where it met the wood.

'You weren't there,' I said.

'I'll be there today,' she said. 'All day.' She tucked her hair behind her ear and pushed up her sleeves. 'See you later.' She went back to her table and soon she was laughing and joking with the other actors.

Stevenson wasn't there at breakfast. Mary served my food. After my last attempts to communicate with her, I didn't bother this time. I kept myself to 'please' and 'thank you' – just like she had done with me. As a result, our relationship settled into a primitive supply and demand pattern. After breakfast I hung around in the dining hall for a while in case Stevenson showed. Then I poked my nose into the kitchen. It was empty so I made

172

my way back to my room.

After about fifteen minutes, there was a knock on the door. Knuckles too delicate to be Stevenson's. It was Mary. But she looked very different. She was wearing stonewashed blue jeans and a pink sweater. Her hair had been pushed up and back by an Alice band and her face was bright. Her pale skin was lit by blusher, eyeliner and pink lipstick.

She smiled.

'There's someone waiting for you,' she said. 'Shall we go?'

We walked downstairs, Mary leading the way, past the kitchen and on into the North Hall. And then we were through the door and outside on the steps. I stopped for a second and closed my eyes, letting the sun and the breeze play on my skin. Mary had already skipped clear of the last stone stair and was striding off towards the western colonnade. I caught up with her.

'What are those rooms used for?' I asked, pointing at the row of windows that lined the colonnade at almost ground level.'

'I've no idea,' she said. 'They look like dungeons, don't they?' She giggled. 'Maybe we'll end up in there if we upset Luke.'

I quite fancied the idea of being imprisoned down there with Mary.

We passed the colonnade and turned into the power yard – triangular, penned in by sheer granite walls that had barely a window between them. The generator was pumping hard. Up close, the sound was fierce. In fact, walking through there was like being in a prison yard and having white noise hurled at you. The walls were a dark triptych painted with mould, damp, moss and dirt. The turbines pounded the ground.

On the far side of the yard, we went down three steps and emerged on to a pathway. On our left there was a concrete area, small and square. It must back on to the kitchens – there were large metal bins standing against the far wall. Ahead of us I could see the path open out on to a small lawn bordered by paving stones. On the far side of that was a large, rectangular building, side-on, made of more dark granite. Above its left-hand wall, the building's roof reached a triangular peak. At the apex was a huge, weather-beaten stone ball. But we weren't going as far as that building – instead we turned into a doorway on our left, which led into a narrow, gloomy corridor. Then we turned right into a bright, high-ceilinged room decked out like an old-fashioned classroom. There were rows of wooden desks. On the walls there were charts showing sections of the gut, cross-sections of blood vessels, muscles, bones and the urino-genital system. At the far end of the room there was a blackboard, covered in a white haze of chalk dust and leaning on a wooden easel. Behind the easel was a dais and behind that a large whiteboard that ran most of the length of the wall. Mary showed me to a desk at the front, a few feet from the easel. On its top was an exercise book with my name on it, and a pencil.

I sat down and opened the book. It was pristine. I ran a finger down the inside of the cover. And with that act I was back at school. A brand new exercise book from the stationery cupboard. Thank you, miss. The last one completed and put away, its job done. The first strokes of the pen across the new smooth surface. 'Make them strong and neat. Each time you open this book it'll be this page you see first. This page that will tell you about yourself.'

Mary was somewhere behind me then, I think, but Catherine was standing in front of me. She was next to the blackboard, only a couple of feet from my desk. Her hair was up, she was wearing glasses, a tight pink sweater and a blue pencil skirt. She had a stick in her hand. She took half a step forward and rapped it on my desk three times. I whipped my hands away in shock.

'Where have you been?' she said. 'Don't be late again. Yes, I know it's hot in here. You'll just have to suffer, I'm afraid. The caretaker's off sick.'

She was looking towards the back of the classroom. I turned round. Mary had gone. But the second actress was there now, leaning against the wall in school uniform, her arms folded.

And then Catherine peeled off her sweater. As she pulled

it over her face, her breasts were pulled tight underneath her white blouse. When she pulled the sweater away I heard the crackle of static electricity. Her hair was tousled now – as if she had just lifted her head from a pillow. Then she shook her shoulders to restore the shape of the blouse, and combed her hair back into place with her fingers.

'Right,' she said and tapped the stick against the blackboard. There was a movement to my left and then the sound of a chair across the floor. The other actress was taking the desk next to me. Her tie was neat inside her closely fitting collar, her face young and innocent without its make-up.

'Today,' said Catherine, 'we're going to learn about the difference between boys and girls. Françoise, I believe you've prepared something for us?'

'Yes, miss,' the other actress said. 'Thank you, miss.'

She turned to me and said:

'For boys, sex is like driving a car. One hand on the steering wheel, the other on the gear stick. Pressing hard on the accelerator. Enjoying the journey – and admiring the view. But you're not paying enough attention to your passenger. Maybe you need some more lessons. The journey has to be satisfying for her, too, you know.'

I could feel Catherine's eyes watching me.

'You're going too fast,' Françoise said. 'There's no rush. Take your time. You'll be glad you did. It'll be even more exciting when you finally reach your destination. Your passenger will be glad, too. In fact she'll love you for it. But maybe you can't manage that? Was that a touch of road rage I saw there? Maybe you need to cool off for a bit. I think we should go home. And put the car back in the garage. We'll come out again another day. Next time you'll be able to plan the route a bit better.' A dreamy look came over her face. 'Wouldn't Christmas be lovely with just the two of us? Me in bed, you on one knee, the snow falling outside the window?'

She folded her arms across her chest.

'But maybe we need to talk,' she said.

And then she brought her arms down to her sides and pressed her palms flat on the wood of the chair.

'In fact maybe we should call it a day.' Her lips were half-open now. The red of her tongue was just visible in the darkness of her mouth.

Catherine was staring at me.

'Maybe we're just not suited,' said Françoise. 'Maybe we're not supposed to be together.'

She looked back at Catherine.

'Thank you, Françoise,' Catherine said. Then she tapped her stick against the blackboard again.

'Now,' she said, 'boys dream about girls. And about women.'

She turned round to the blackboard and wrote 'Dreams' at the top. She had to stretch upwards and stand on tiptoe. Her body elongated, sharpened and tensed. Her thighs grew tighter and her heel left the floor.

She turned back to us. Her face was slightly flushed.

'You may, for instance,' she said, looking straight at me, 'find yourself fantasising about your teacher. But it would never do to act on those fantasies. Do you understand? Good. Françoise, do you have something else to say?'

Catherine smiled at Françoise, who smiled back. For a second they seemed locked into a private joke. Then Françoise turned to me again.

'Yes, miss. Thank you, miss. I can feel the world opening up for me. I feel the strength of the flowers and the water and the earth and the sun. I feel roots spreading into the soil and sap rising, leaves unfolding and chemicals dissolving. It's my world, miss. I know so much more than he does, I'm so much more in touch with life. I have a secret power that he can't even dream of. This whole thing between him and me is no one else's business, miss, it's personal. After we've been out to the fields today, after we've come back – tonight, maybe – I'll feel differently about it, I know that already. That's why I've made him swear he won't say anything. No one must ever know. I don't want this coming back to haunt me. Because when I grow up I want to be someone.'

Catherine had been writing on the board during Françoise's speech. Underneath 'Dreams' she had added: 'My world',

'Secret power', 'To be someone'. There were chalk stains on the front of her skirt where she had rubbed against the board.

'Thank you, Françoise,' said Catherine, putting down her stick. 'Very nice. Well, children, that's all for today. I hope you've learnt something. I'm sure I have. Now, off you go and enjoy yourselves.'

Françoise was smiling again. She stood up and held out her hand. I stood, too. She led me across the room. Just before we got to the door she turned and whispered: 'Meet you behind the bike sheds.' Then she walked off down the corridor.

Mary was outside the door, waiting for me.

'Are you ready?' she asked.

We went back outside and turned towards the lawn and the large hall. The flowers in the tight green rectangle of grass were red, yellow and blue. There was a bench there. Mary sat down. I joined her.

'How long have you worked here, Mary?' I asked. 'Were you working here before Haines arrived?'

'Yes,' she replied.

'So you were working for Catherine?'

'Yes,' she said firmly. Then she turned her head away and stared at the ground, as if something had caught her attention. I followed her eyes but there was nothing there.

'What's she like?' I asked.

'Oh, she's nice,' she replied, lifting her head again and smiling now.

'Does she talk about Haines much?'

'Sometimes,' she said.

'What sort of things does she say?' I asked.

'Well,' she said, 'I remember her once telling me a bit about his childhood.'

'Pretty dull, I'd imagine, wasn't it?' I asked.

'Oh, you'd be surprised,' she replied. 'Really you would.' She turned towards me and put a hand on the bench between us. Her eyes lit up. 'When he was little he had this thing about wanting to run away and join the circus. You know what some kids are like. Well, near where he lived there was a wintering site for one of the big troupes. He used to disappear sometimes, just vanish from the house. His mother would find him there, wandering around, looking in all the empty cages, staring at all the equipment, all packed up.' She was looking past me now, back towards the Hall. 'Then, one spring, when the circus was about to set off on tour, he went missing again. He'd gone with it, stowed away. His parents guessed what had happened. His dad found out where the circus was and drove there. Found him curled up asleep in the back of a truck.'

She looked across to the far side of the lawn where a blackbird was staring at us, its head tilted.

'I'll tell you something else,' she said excitedly. 'A few years later, when he was sixteen or seventeen, there was a trial at the Old Bailey. A man who'd been involved with the Angry Brigade. Matthews, his name was. They'd caught him for tax evasion or something but they really wanted him because of what he knew. Before he went to court they interrogated him. He was rumoured to be telling everything in return for a light sentence. On the day the trial started, Luke went up on the train. He sat in the visitors' gallery.' Her eyes twinkled. 'You can see him, can't you, leaning over the rail, staring at Matthews, trying to read his mind? When they broke for lunch he got talking to one of the warders who had brought Matthews to court. Luke told him that he was a politics student interested in what had been going on in Britain in the seventies. The warder was a bit sniffy but Luke managed to sweet-talk him into passing a note to Matthews. After Matthews was convicted and sent to jail they started writing. When he got out a couple of years later, they began to meet. And Luke discovered that there was plenty Matthews had kept back. Things that would make your jaw drop. Things that would make your eyes pop out of your head.'

She looked at her watch again.

'Right,' she said. 'Let's go.'

We walked to the end of the lawn, down a couple of steps, and past an empty conservatory on our left. As we came up to the grim-looking granite building, the large stone ball on its roof began to look precarious, as if it might roll off any minute and crush whoever was underneath it. We had come round on to the stone path that runs along the south side of the Hall. I looked to my left. I could see the Hall there, tall, frowning, chin jutting out over its grounds. We crossed the path on to a rougher, wider one which led into the woods that ran down towards the lake. Soon there were thick trees and undergrowth on either side of us. Mary was singing quietly to herself – 'What Becomes of the Broken-Hearted?' Ahead of us, through the wood, we could see part of a stone and glass building. Then, with a curl of the path and a sudden clearing of the trees, it was there in front of us.

It was a three-storey building the colour of cold lava. Pictures of the trees were reflected on the windows. We walked towards a stiff glass door that Mary had to shove hard to open, and then into an empty ground-floor area with a staircase which arched back towards the first floor.

It was absolutely quiet in there. As we walked towards the stairs, I looked through the windowed wall to our right and saw thick, dark-green foliage, hard against the glass – as if the undergrowth were trying to force its way in. As we walked up, our feet barely moved on the shallow steps – it was like travelling on an escalator. The building's next level gradually came into view as we reached the top of the staircase – a large lounge area in an 'E' shape. Above us and stretching down towards the far end of the lounge, there was a much larger, bare-wood staircase that led to the top floor. We turned back on ourselves and walked towards the front of the building.

There were seat units around the walls here, with dark, flat cushions. In the far corner, her arm draped across the back of one of the seats, was Françoise. She was staring out of the window, into the trees.

We went over to her. I sat where Mary pointed – opposite Françoise – and Mary took a seat a few feet away.

Françoise was wearing a ruched pink top, a crumpled puffball skirt and thin, very high heels. There was a table in front of her with a half-empty bottle of champagne and a single glass.

We sat in silence. Finally Françoise turned towards me. Then she reached up to her ears – and pulled out a pair of headphones. She had been plugged into an iPod.

Slowly she recrossed her legs, watching me as she moved.

'I love to be around money,' she said. 'Big houses and fast cars. Designer clothes and society parties. Boyfriends with platinum credit cards. September 16th 1992. Black Wednesday. Poor Daddy lost everything. I was lucky, though. I survived. Because Daddy had already made his introductions for me – back when they were still worth something. The contacts were in the bag. They were money in the bank. I called some friends in the music business. Got a band together and made a record. A guy with a perm and gold records on the wall produced it. A smooth-skinned PR man with an office in Soho sold it. Poor Daddy, some of those press articles didn't show him in a very good light. But he didn't mind. He sat tight and thought of the cash. It was nice to be able to repay him a little.' She brought a hand up into the air and flexed her fingers. Satisfied with the perfect turquoise nail polish, she carried on with her story. 'After we had our number one it was a sports car for me and a Jag for him. Everyone loved me. Red carpets, ribbons, champagne and photographers. Rose petals and confetti. Once you've made it in the pop business, all you need to do is make sure that you're seen. Be beautiful. Be extravagant. And speak to the papers and the magazines – but remember the last thing they want is the truth. And if anyone turns up from your past – stamp on him.'

She folded her hands in her lap. 'And now there's a vacancy at the heart of the nation. For Queen of Hearts. Queen of the South. England is calling. England needs me.'

As she reached out to pour herself another glass of champagne, Mary got to her feet and plucked me by the elbow.

We left Françoise to it and headed up the staircase to the top floor. Once we had climbed a few steps it began to feel chilly. The light, too, seemed to dip a little. Up at the top of the stairs, we walked into another lounge area, similar to the one below, but with tinted windows and a cool current coming from an invisible air-conditioning system. The lounge stretched out around us on all sides, with no staircase to interrupt it. There were seats lining the windows here, too, but they were cream-coloured and made an unbroken circuit round the room. It was like an observation lounge up there, but all you could see through the windows was leaves and branches, and hints of a sky dyed charcoal-grey. There was only one person looking out, and that was Catherine.

She was sitting directly above Françoise's seat a floor below. On the table next to her, though, was a bottle of gin, and she was wearing a plain black dress. Mary led me over to her.

As Françoise had, she waited a few moments before she turned to speak to us. It looked as though what Catherine was dragging herself away from, though, was her own self-absorption.

Mary and I sat in the same positions as we had downstairs, so I was opposite Catherine. Her face looked pale.

'Yes,' she said, 'I had a perfect childhood. And now I've grown up I live in a dream home. In Notting Hill. With William. Last weekend we decorated – plastering over the cracks that have appeared in the walls. We used to drive out to the countryside and walk. We've collected fossils, the skull of a fox, a pile of peacock feathers and a rabbit's foot. We refuse dinner invitations and never send out our own. We drink hot chocolate before bed. We keep our old lives in a box. Photos of weddings, holidays and dinner parties. Always in the background there are other, nameless people. People passing us by on a beach, standing at the back of bars, sitting in shadows in restaurants. At night I close my eyes and I see all his old girlfriends – next to me, inside me, rising up from me.'

She looked out of the window.

'He's seeing someone else,' she continued, eyes on the tableau of unmoving trees. 'It started three months ago. But I don't care. I keep busy. Looking after our house. Trips to the shops. And I've got a new interest. I'm seeing someone, too.'

She turned back towards me.

'I keep thinking about you. Again and again. Yesterday afternoon when we met, we talked and talked. But then you left. Last night the girls came round. Martina, Jessica, Natasha and Sue. I prayed they would leave. I paid no attention to what

181

they said, their laughter went floating out of the window. I wanted them to go so I could sleep. Because then I'd be with you again. All night, in my dreams. What happens when your lover starts seeing someone else? You set about trying to ruin his life. Little things to start with. To get into the swing of it. Until you know what you're doing. There's this house in Notting Hill. The police are digging in the back garden.'

She reached for the bottle of gin and poured herself a drink.

'Do you remember Billy?' she said. 'He and I used to tell each other everything. Because we could come right up close day after day, look each other in the eye and talk and not get scared. We went out drinking every weekend. Drinking and talking and waking up next to each other fully clothed at midday, with the sun beating down on our pounding heads. Each weekend slipping further into the world we had created. A world of sexless intimacy with a population of two. Next weekend, we used to say, we'll get in the car and just drive. And when we run out of petrol we'll run. And then we'll walk, and then we'll crawl. I had a dream once. Standing on a bridge over the Thames with two dead boys who had charmed me. The Deverell Twins. Standing in my curls and ribbons and bows. They pointed to their underwater kingdom. They showed me the night sky reflected in the dark water. Reach out, they said, reach out and pick a star. Put it in your pocket and jump into the sky. I was their child bride. I flew off the bridge, my sea-wings tucked in to my sides. Diving, falling, flying. Then spinning and whirling. Then swimming and flying again, flying deep underneath the waves. A white Victorian nightdress billowing in the underwater current. In the sea wind.'

She leant towards me and grabbed my hand.

'Let's go somewhere,' she said. 'Shall we? Let's go out. Let's dance through the streets! Paint your face. Make yourself look special. I'll help you. Where shall we go? Let's go down to the sea. There'll be no one there. We'll dance in the moonlight.'

She dropped my hand again. Then she reached out for her glass and took a drink. She dabbed her mouth with the back of her hand, and then wiped the hand on her dress.

'A holiday by the seaside,' she said. 'I was fifteen. A cottage above the town, perched on a hill. A hand round the door, a fiver furled between two fingers. "Here's some money for chips and ice cream. Mummy's going to have a lie down." I walked down to the sea. The smell of salt water and seaweed. Rain. From the other end of the beach a man and a woman coming towards me. There was a space between them as they walked. Slowly we got closer. When they got near enough to see my face they stopped. And they both stared. His mouth was open. Her face was white. I walked round them, watching them, and they turned with me. I began to walk away from them, backwards, staring as they stared at me. Then he looked at her. And he reached out his hand. And she took it. And then they turned and they carried on walking, side by side, hand in hand. 'When I got back to our cottage, I handed back the fiver. "No, Mum,' I said, "I didn't talk to anyone. There was no one there. No one at all."'

Catherine took my hand again. Hers had grown cold.

'I'm scared now,' she said. 'I want to go home. But they're searching the garden. Help me.'

As I walked back along the south side of the Hall, down by the lake the distant figure of one of the gardeners was unloading something from a rowing boat into a wheelbarrow.

I was the only one in the dining hall at lunch. Almost as soon as I sat down, Stevenson appeared with a plate of one of Henri's vegetarian specialities – spaghetti in a thick, sweet tomato and onion sauce.

'Here we are, sir,' he said as he put the food down in front of me. 'I believe that Henri has surpassed himself on your behalf today. How was the morning?'

'Thank you, Stevenson,' I replied. 'It was very instructive.'

'Ah, I am pleased, sir. Pleased that we are continuing to inform. And dare one ask, sir, how work on the book is going?'

'Things are coming along,' I said. 'You'll feature, of course.'

He had been wiping one of my knives on a white napkin.

Now he stopped.

'Is that absolutely necessary, sir?' he asked.

'You play such a large part in everything that goes on here,' I replied. I reached for the pepper grinder, but Stevenson was there before me. He began to twist it slowly, his hands circling a foot above my plate.

'What do you think your father would have said about you appearing in a book?' I asked.

'I doubt whether he would have been very impressed, sir. My presence on the printed, bound page would have seemed to him inappropriate and anomalous. "A place for everything and everything in its place," was his golden rule.'

'Not, "Do as you would be done by"?'

'Sadly, no, sir. If I may be permitted to say something possibly less than charitable about the old chap, that rule applies only to those freer, in either fact or spirit, than Father was. He set his own standards for dealing with those who were his social superiors – and, I am afraid, for those he considered beneath him.'

'You seem to be putting yourself in the same category as your father, Stevenson, when it comes to education, or the lack of it. But you must have been to school.'

'Certainly, sir, I received a perfectly reasonable education in the comprehensive system. But it meant little to my father. He showed no interest in my schooling. For him my time until sixteen was a period of limbo. As far as he was concerned, my life would only really begin when I left school and followed him into butlery. As he himself was uneducated, he preferred to believe that I was the same – ignoring the evidence of my school books and the reports that he received from my teachers. He refused to acknowledge the improvement in the level and range of my conversation as my knowledge deepened and my horizons broadened. He turned a blind eye to the extra-curricular reading and study in which I had become enthusiastically engaged. Autodidacticism was not something of which he approved. We are given our station in life, he believed. We should occupy it, and may grow to fill it, but must never attempt to leave it.'

'I can see you, after school,' I said, 'heading down to the library with your books. When the other kids were playing football and fighting.'

'Oh, believe me, sir, there was plenty of time for that, too.'

Stevenson's tone had changed. I had obviously touched a nerve.

'Was yours a rough school, Stevenson?' I asked.

'For some of the pupils,' he replied. 'Now, sir,' he added, whisking my plate away from me, 'I believe it is time to move on.' I hadn't finished – my knife and fork were still spread across my half-eaten food.

'Move on?' I asked.

'Indeed, sir, the afternoon entertainment will be getting under way shortly. Oh, did no one tell you? How remiss. Yes, we are to be privileged to witness a performance by Mr Haines himself. A car will be waiting for you at the north entrance in a quarter of an hour. I look forward to seeing you then, sir.'

And then both he and my spaghetti were gone.

When I walked out on to the steps fifteen minutes later, Françoise was already there. At the foot of the steps was an old MG in British Racing Green, with its top down.

'Hi,' I said. 'What's happening?'

'Get in,' she said.

We sped off. Low to the ground, I could feel each bump of the uneven surface – the suspension needed some urgent attention. Next to me, Françoise blurred as she bounced up and down, a wide smile on her face. She was wearing dark glasses and a silk scarf that flew behind her in the wind.

We passed through the arch and out on to the familiar stony road. Soon we had left the light aircraft and the wrecked car behind. We crossed the bridge and flew past the orange castle, through the trees, on a narrow road that I hadn't noticed before. When we came to a halt it was in front of another temple, larger than the one where I had seen Françoise and her stolen baby, and witnessed Catherine's miserable Sunday. In front of it, a stage had been erected.

On the grass below the stage were two rows of chairs. By

the chairs and across the field behind, in which a film camera had been set up, people were milling about. There were tables, too, spread with cold food. Françoise parked the car halfway down the field, next to a 4x4 and at right angles to a truck full of electrical equipment that was being unloaded. We got out and began walking up the slope towards the people and the seats.

At the sides of the stage were round lights on slim metal gantries. On it stood two large, metal-framed beds, in front of a white backdrop, draped with a trio of huge banners, that extended from roof to floor. On one of these was a swastika, on another a Union Jack and on the third a pentagram.

Up on the stage I could see Haines, gesturing to a man next to him in an open-necked shirt and shades. Haines was wearing flared jeans and a scruffy denim jacket with 'Pink Floyd', 'Soft Machine' and 'Tangerine Dream' written on it. Catherine was there, too, standing on his other side. She had her arm round his waist. As we got closer, I recognised the other actors. They were all there – including the Kid and the Killer. These two, though, were standing apart from the others. The Killer's mask was attached to a belt round his waist. At the back of the stage, running diagonally from a corner of the floor to a point high up amongst the lights, was a thin staircase.

As we got closer to the seats, the Kid left the Killer and came towards us. He was smiling – a sunny, childlike smile. 'Good afternoon, sir. Good afternoon, madam,' he said. Giving us a tiny bow, he handed over a couple of gold-embossed invitation cards. In flamboyant writing with Elizabethan curls they said:

'You are cordially invited to a non-entertainment: "A brief history of the twentieth century."'

The Kid went back to the Killer, and Françoise led us to the middle of the front row of seats. She pointed to one of them. When I sat down she walked away without a word, back towards the assorted film types gathered behind. She started talking to some guy in a thin leather jacket.

There was still a certain amount of activity on the stage, but it seemed to be decreasing. The area was clearing – Haines and the guy who I took to be the director of the performance were walking down a set of wooden steps at the side, back on to the grass. There was no one else sitting with me on the chairs.

And then the stage was empty – and, with a series of echoing thumps, the lights came on. Suddenly there was highlighting and emphasis on the beds, the banners and the staircase. I looked to my right and there was Haines, at the bottom of the stairs, with an acoustic guitar in his hand. He was wearing a long-haired wig, blond and straggly. I looked behind me again. Everyone had gone. All that was left was a single cameraman and his camera. Then I felt a gloved hand take my own. It was Catherine. She was wearing a white muslin dress and a cloche hat. She sat down beside me. I opened my mouth to speak to her but she put a finger to her lips and smiled. Then from somewhere behind me I heard a shout of 'Action!' and Haines began to walk up the steps.

Once he was on the stage he made straight for a microphone stand in front of the bed on the right. Positioned behind it, he began to play – on his guitar was stencilled the word 'Auteurs'. And then he began to sing. The song was 'Satan Wants Me' and he was dressed as the student who narrates the novel.

As he sang about Aleister Crowley and the invocation of demons, another figure entered the stage behind him, a bald man in Edwardian mountaineering gear with a large '666' on his back, who made his way to the bottom of the staircase. When the song moved on to Kenneth Anger and the Stones, and the Dalai Lama and the Nazis, the figure began very slowly to climb the stairs, picking his way with a tiny hammer. As Haines talked of fathering a child for Satan, Catherine got up and walked over to the stairs at the side of the stage. Lifting her skirts from her feet, she climbed the steps. Walking across behind Haines, she gave him a pat on the arse. Then she took a seat on the bed at the centre of the stage.

As the song's final verse began, with L Ron Hubbard and Tom Cruise rubbished in favour of Jimmy Page, a movement to my left caught my eye. I turned to see Adolf Hitler strutting towards me. It was the actor who had played the English fascist in the garden. He looked authentic. He sat down next to me. My side went numb. His trousers had those ridiculous bulges at the side. The material was brushing against my leg. Round his waist was a black holster with a gun nestling inside. Maybe it came from the museum in the garden. It looked like genuine Nazi kit. I could have been touching the clothes of a mass-murderer. Although I was sitting next to an actor – and one I'd seen playing many other parts – he was something completely different wearing that stuff. You can't dress like that and get made up with that hairstyle and moustache without surrendering a part of yourself. As the song ended, Catherine lifted a hand in my direction. For a second I wondered if I was going to be dragged into all this in some way, but then Hitler stood up, gave me a creepy tap on the thigh with a gloved hand that seemed to pass right through my leg, and set off to join her. As he did, Crowley, at the back of the stage, finally reached the top of the ladder. He sat there, perched, looking down at the action – and lit a joint. Hitler was sitting on the bed next to Catherine now, who had made room for him, patting the space next to her that she had made.

Haines had launched into another song from his solo album, *Das Capital* – 'The Mitford Sisters' – pausing only to bend down and grab a peaked cap from the boards in front of him. He stuck it on top of the blond wig. Two more of the actors came on from the wings – Françoise and the actor who had played the husband in the semi. He was wearing a large lapel badge saying 'BUF'. Hitler and Catherine leapt up to greet them. Catherine was obviously playing Unity Mitford, while the other two were her sister Diana and Oswald Mosley. The four of them started pirouetting around the stage. Within a few bars, though, the dance had descended into a display of goose-stepping.

The song's centrepiece is based on Powell and Pressburger's film *A Matter of Life and Death*. For this the actors stopped dancing and arranged themselves in a semi-circle, holding hands as a red light hit a balcony that ran along the roof of the temple. Inside the crimson circle, the actor who looked like Haines, now dressed as the film's British pilot who is falling from the sky, mouthed his last words on earth as Haines himself sang them to June, the earthbound wireless operator the airman loves.

As Diana and Mosley watched from the side of the stage, Unity and Hitler waltzed in front of them while the song drew to its conclusion. When Haines hit the final chord, the actors headed for the wings – and almost collided with a roller-skating figure coming on. It was the actor who looked like Haines again – he had kept the airman's flamboyant moustache but had whipped off his flying jacket to reveal a 'Queen Victoria' T-shirt – and he was gliding across the stage, hands clasped behind him. Haines now went into the final 'history song' from *Das Capital*, 'Bugger Bognor'. The roller skater was George V. At the back of the stage, Crowley had left his perch and had begun climbing back down the ladder. Stage right now, Françoise came back on, her hair hanging loose, wearing a long white nightdress. She clambered on to the bed and drew her legs up to her body. The actor who had played Mosley, buttoning up a white coat on to which he had transferred his badge, emerged from the wings and stood next to the bed, encouraging Françoise in her labour. He was joined by Mary, dressed in a nurse's uniform. Then I could see the actor who had played Hitler, now wearing a dinner jacket, slip back on to the stage and crawl underneath the bed.

As Françoise screamed and gave birth, the bed split apart and the actor hidden underneath rose up through the gap and stood there, placing a crown on his head. The 'tache had gone and the Hitler hairstyle had been combed aside. It was Edward VIII. Crowley had now reached the bottom of the ladder and his arms and fingers began to fly through the air as he fired off a succession of obscene gestures. Françoise got up from the bed and left with the other actors, leaving only Edward on the stage. Edward moved sharply away from the bed and stood at the front, adjusting his collar. His trousers were still very obviously Hitler's. Then Catherine came back on. She looked a little plainer now. The jewellery she had been wearing before had been removed, a Stars and Stripes emblem was pinned to her chest and she wore a short-haired wig – she had become Wallis Simpson. She walked over to Edward and they embraced. Then they moved over, arm in arm, to the far side of the stage, almost bumping into George, who was now stumbling on his roller skates towards the second bed. He collapsed there as the song ended – Haines voicing his exhausted 'Bugger Bognor' for him – before expiring while clutching his stomach. Then Haines, Edward, Wallis and Crowley all converged in front of the bed, where they were joined by George, and linked arms. They all took a bow. I applauded – alone. The actors walked off stage in single file.

After they had gone, I sat there in the silence, waiting for them to come back out and for the film crew, technicians and hangers-on to gather again.

But no one appeared. I looked round. The cameraman had vanished, too. Maybe the actors were all in the temple? Maybe they were expecting me to join them there? I got up and walked over.

The temple was quiet and still. I walked up the steps to the front door and looked through the window. It was dark inside. I turned the handle but the door was locked. I banged on the window. No one came.

Then I walked round the back of the building. There were a couple of small windows set into the stone there, but too high to see through. There were tyremarks on the grass – there must have been two or three vehicles parked there earlier.

I looked around me. The whole place was empty. There was no point in staying there.

I began to walk.

I decided that I would head across the field in front of the temple until I reached the path that led to the wrecked car. Then, once I got close to the arch leading to the Hall, I would cut through the trees and come out on the road that flanked the fields to the north. I had remembered something that Stevenson had told me at lunch – about this north road being best avoided at the moment, due to some ongoing repair work. Maybe there was a bit more to it than that.

I arrived on the stone and baked clay of this unmarked road without seeing another soul.

For a quarter of a mile it continued dead straight, the woods to my right, fields to the left.

But then, instead of heading up towards the hillier territory to the north of the estate, it began to swing round to the right, into the trees. It seemed to be aiming for the densest part of the wood. Soon all I could see was an impenetrable screen of foliage and undergrowth. The curve of the road was becoming tighter, too, now – I could only see a few yards ahead. It must, I thought suddenly, be dragging me round towards the river. And then I heard a faint sound – of distant, mechanised pumping. But then I stopped dead. Because there was a man in front of me, blocking my path. And he was holding a machine gun. He was wearing a black uniform. I couldn't turn, couldn't run. Couldn't move. He walked towards me. Behind him, through the tangle of branches and vegetation, I saw a hint of light reflecting off water.

'Lost?' he said. His voice was matter-of-fact, businesslike. I nodded.

'Best turn round and go back the way you came, then.'

The gun hung low in his hands, his feet were loosely planted. His face was expressionless.

I did what he said.

After thirty seconds, I stopped and turned, wondering if he was following me. But there was nothing there but branches, leaves and the stony road.

As I headed back towards the Hall, the pumping sound faded.

The seconds and the yards began to accumulate. Soon the pattern of the trees became recognisable, the surface of the road familiar. Then the stone of the arch appeared ahead. And then the solid vastness of the Hall – my current home – began to open up there like a giant bird spreading its wings.

Inside the North Hall, I leant against the door and let the cool air and stone draw the heat from me.

There was no one around as I headed for my room. The only hint of life was the smell of the newly waxed corridor.

No Catherine at supper, no actors, no Stevenson, no Mary.

Henri brought me my food himself. It gave me an opportunity to thank him in person – and to say how much

I always enjoyed his meals. He looked genuinely delighted, smiling warmly, nodding profusely. But he didn't say a word. I have never heard Henri speak. Is he deaf or dumb, perhaps? Or a non-English speaker? He rested a hand on my shoulder for a second before he left.

Time to crash out. Lots of things going through my head. Feeling out of it. Out of the loop. Out of everything.

Editor's note —

Well, the writer seems a trifle distressed. So let us return to happier times. At the bright beginning of a new day. Control + home. Ah!

But what is this? A new morning dawns over this magnificent palace and what does the writer do? He sits in his luxurious quarters and dreams of his sordid bedsit! Are we boring him? Is he becoming homesick? And then, when his mind does turn to the paradise in which he has found himself, what strange thoughts he has about what is occurring around him! That such an odd person should think that what we do down here is peculiar beggars belief. And how sad that, having recognised the ludic nature of our activities, he feels unable to join in.

The writer dreams of having a taxi waiting to drive him back to the station at the end of his stay. But what if this vehicle – for surely he must realise that there is only one out here – is already booked up for that day? Or what if someone else wants to go somewhere or do something? Or what if it has been decided that, on this day, it would merely be better for it to sit in its lean-to garage, gathering moisture from the drip, drip, drip through the hole in the roof above and settling a little lower on the ground as the air slowly seeps from the weakening valves of its tyres? Anyway, these dreams of escape really are not going to help the writer – he should be straining every fibre to get a grip on the reality of his situation.

Incidentally, much of *Seance on a Wet Afternoon* was shot by director Bryan Forbes from the open door of a taxi. The film was also one of the first on which Mr Forbes made extensive use of his cameras' zoom facility, which allowed him to film the action while remaining far away from it – sometimes from the tops of buildings. This is a technique that Mr Haines has used extensively on his own project.

The writer's infatuation with Catherine is pitiful in an orphaned puppy dog way. And his pining after Stevenson in the dining room is rather pathetic, too, don't you think? Especially for a man who claims to be a loner. His attempts to engage with Stevenson on the level of some kind of imagined friendship are becoming embarrassing.

The writer believes that, after he is gone, the world of the Hall will just carry on without him. But how could it, dear writer? – you are, of course, the centre of all our lives!

Stevenson has absented himself again from breakfast. A question of priorities. Things continue to move on apace.

Mary has been told to snap out of it and to make herself more accommodating to the writer. It is not her job – any more – to be reticent with him. Catherine is unhappy with taking all the responsibility for toying with his affections. Mary must shoulder more of the burden. But surely this has not had immediate results? Surely the writer is not falling for Mary, too, is he? Already? Although I must say that she may have led him on a little fast with that line about being imprisoned with him down in the 'dungeons'. The thought of incarceration seems to have engendered in him more thoughts of penal confinement, though, viz. his comment about the 'prison exercise yard'. This can only be a good thing. Let us hope, too, that the little lesson in the classroom will have sorted him out, sexually. Maybe the drenching in female hormones administered collectively by the young ladies will have helped. I noted Catherine's veiled warning regarding the writer fantasising about his 'teacher'. He should heed it. The thought of this delicate creature being taken prisoner by the writer's imagination and chained up inside a dark cell in his mind is deeply distressing to me. In fact I can barely hold my swollen pen to this piece of virgin-white paper for long enough to pen my response. You cad, sir!!

Mary treads a fine line with her stories about Mr Haines's

youth. Where she got them from I really don't know. Maybe she even believes they are true! Who knows what passes through that pretty little head of hers, or what takes root there? We must applaud her efforts in coming up with them.

Today's performances in the classroom and the conference centre were based around two estimable records by Black Box Recorder – *Facts of Life* and *Passionoia*. On these two works, Messrs Haines and Moore have managed to refine their analysis and exposition of the life of the modern Englishwoman to a degree of almost psychic identification.

Sadly, James Jefferson Griff IV did not live long enough to see his dream fulfilled for the conference centre that he had built. He had hoped annually to fill this modern structure, buried among the trees, with the world's greatest experts on the life cycle and behaviour of the urban pigeon – for which he had conceived a fascination while visiting Trafalgar Square on a youthful holiday to this land. Someone else will have to take on that mighty task. It is unlikely to be Mr Haines.

JJ's wife was Constance, only issue from the loins of the third Earl. The Earl's wife gave birth to her daughter even as her husband was making his fateful entry into Franco's Spain (see below). Constance was a wild child, and a succession of Norland nannies was unable to tame her. Discovering, as a teenager, that her womb was destined to remain for ever barren, she embarked upon an early adulthood of widespread promiscuity. After the death of her mother, she lived it up on what was left of the Earls' money, before finally deciding in her mid-forties that it was time to find herself a rich old man. A short holiday in Texas was sufficient to achieve this end and she returned leading JJGIV by the leather thong which he wore round his neck instead of a tie. JJ had made his money from a chain of gutter-scraping rags but professed never to read any of them himself. He was a sucker for English brains, beauty and a defunct baronetcy.

Constance relied on her husband pegging it soon after their marriage. But sadly it was she who was first to go. Seeking sexual satisfaction away from him at the earliest polite opportunity, she indulged her libido to the full by taking a course of Dehydroepiandrosterone supplements and working her way through a procession of sleek, athletic young men. (No need for the writer to take any of that stuff, eh, Mary?) Six months later Constance was dead of a heart attack.

Yes, Stevenson is an educated man. School of life, university of hard knocks etc. One day he was cornered outside the school gate by those hard cases Pattinson, Adler and Moon. The first had his bollocks crushed, the second's cigarette was stubbed out in his eye, the third suffered a cauliflower ear, scrambled-egg nose and kidney lip. But Stevenson was in the clear. Pattinson, Adler and Moon's account numbered ten in the 'gang' that had rumbled them. And anyway no one would have believed that anyone could have done all that on his own.

Stevenson's father worked for an aristocrat with an attachment to Germany – he felt she had been harshly dealt with at Versailles – and an instinctive yearning for the return to tradition and order promised by Adolf Hitler. There was a lot of it about in upper-class circles in those days.

In 1945, allegations were made that the third Earl had been a Nazi sympathiser, and things began to go badly wrong for him. Although the allegations were never proved, he was forced to spend the post-war years abroad, and succumbed to a series of hypochondriacal attacks for which he sought quack cures in strange sanatoria. On arriving, as we have just heard, in Franco's Spain, he proceeded to call at a clinic outside Seville in order to change his blood. With the switch from blue to red, though, went his aristocratic immunity to common disease. The blood was infected – purposely, one wonders? – and the Earl died a nasty death of typhoid. Having failed to sire a male heir, his line passed to Constance.

Das Capital – the last record before the *Luke Haines is Dead* farewell boxed set. The writer seems more alone than ever in this sequence. It is as if, metaphorically speaking, everything – and everyone – is above him. And looking down on him. He knows that Mr Haines is dressed as the student narrator of *Satan Wants Me*. Does this mean that he has got round to reading this masterful novel? Sadly, I think not. The writer shows all the propensity of the book's narrator to fall under a spell, but none of his ability to fight off that influence – and then, in counter-attack, to extend his own.

Yes, *Das Capital*. A collection of re-recordings of Auteurs classics, together with 'Satan' and a couple of new songs about England, the thirties and fascism – all backed by an orchestra. Bliss! 'Das Capital' is Nazi London. On the front cover of the insert for the CD Mr Haines is portrayed as the brooding genius he is. Inside it he is Rudolph Valentino once more. And also an English curmudgeon by the seaside. Turning pink in the sun as the local kids take the piss. There are many sides to his complex character. Where the disc fits into the case of the CD it makes a bullet hole in the middle of Mr Haines's head – and on the bullet is a photo of his old self.

Incidentally, the co-option of *A Matter of Life and Death* into 'The Mitford Sisters' predates Bracewell's similar use of it in his *England is Mine*.

Mr Haines has, of course, he tells us, retired from public service. But will he nevertheless somehow find a way to reinsert himself into British history, I wondered when I spoke to him? His reply was surprisingly forthright and gives us all hope that the creative art of matching words to music is still flourishing, in secret, within the walls of the Hall:

'I shall be undertaking more time travel. The idea of writing about hidden or forgotten bits of history is appealing in this age of ill-remembered culture. I have never thought that a song has to be rooted in any kind of reality. Assumptions of what songs are supposed to be only come from critics who can't write songs.'

Well said, sir, and, on behalf of the nation, thank you for that faint ray of hope in these dark days. Mr Haines's final line here reminds me of another gem from Mr Whistler:

'I hold that none but an artist can be a competent critic.'

The encroachment of military violence, in the form of the 'armed guard' (a costume barely worthy of an amateur dramatics society and a toy gun can still cast a vicious spell over the slow-witted, it seems) is an interesting development in the writer's life. Viewers of Mr Haines's completed film will take particular interest in this sequence, enjoying, I am sure, the aerial shot from the small balloon that the writer seems to have failed to spot, tethered above the trees of Murder Park. The writer's relief at getting back to the Hall – no matter how well disguised – is pitiful.

The writer claims never to have heard Henri speak. This is a lie. The two have communicated in secret. The situation is being kept under review.

I was expecting to have seen another message from 'Klaus' by now. Somewhat strangely, I feel, none has appeared. No matter. I have had a few moments to spare and have come up with my own version!

I therefore humbly offer the following:

'Mein freund,

I am happy to receive your message.

I met Luke for the first time in Switzerland. In Zurich. He was touring with the Servants. I was on holiday from my work station in Berlin and visiting old haunts of exiled revolutionary heroes such as Vladimir Ilyich Ulyanov and Tristan Tzara. I always hoped that Luke will one day use Dadaist techniques for confronting the audience but my hopes have not been realised. I was sure always that random acts of violence with a gun in the concert theatres of England will create very good publicity for the Auteurs. This night (like many nights this tour, I think) Luke was drinking much and talking with much freedom. We talked about the revolution, and about Andreas Baader and Ulrike Meinhof. When I informed Luke that Ulrike was the godmother of my old friend Berndt he was very interested. I told Luke that Ulrike was once hiding in our Reichsstrasse apartment for three days. I told him I have photos of Ulrike smoking and drinking deep underground in our basement in lamplight and candlelight. Luke and I had a wild evening in Zurich. It ended when we visited a bar filled with many media men and women. He was very drunk and caused a disturbance. We were put heavily into the street by two big bald men. The next day I gave my address to him and he did the same with

me. Later we communicated more.
     And later I will communicate with you again!
     There is much more to say, but now I must go.
     Gute nacht, kamerad! Schlaf gut!

                                   Klaus.'

Day Eight

I opened my door this morning and Mary was standing there, back in her maid's uniform. She smiled and asked if I was ready for breakfast.

On the way down I asked her how long she had been there.

'Why, I had just arrived when you opened the door, of course,' she said. 'I was just about to knock. You gave me quite a shock, I must say.'

Downstairs it was Mary who served me. After she had delivered a rack of warm toast, she hovered around.

'Did you hear about the break-in?' she asked, pretending to dust the table.

'No,' I said, pausing as I buttered my first slice of toast.

'The servants have all been talking about it,' she fluttered. 'I hope nothing was stolen. We haven't seen Mr Stevenson all morning. I do hope he's all right. I hope he didn't disturb them and do something silly. You know how brave he is.'

'Oh, I'm sure he's fine,' I said. 'The boss has probably got him doing something.'

At that point Mary gave a start and looked towards the door. I turned round – Stevenson was standing there. As Mary slipped behind me, he bellowed at her:

'Mary – what are you doing, girl? Have you no work to do?'

She scuttled past him, giving him a wide berth, and then out of the door in the direction of the kitchens.

Stevenson came towards me.

'I do apologise for the intrusion, sir,' he said. 'I do hope Mary was not disturbing you. I will have a stern word with her and remind her of her position here.'

'No, no, please don't, Stevenson,' I said. 'She was really no trouble at all. It was my fault for encouraging her. Please don't blame her.'

Stevenson took a step closer. He bent his head towards me. He must have been wearing a new collar. The skin around it was chafed.

'You encouraged her?' he asked. 'What possessed you to do that? It is grossly unfair to undermine her in this way. You have taken advantage of a decent girl.'

'Yes,' I said. 'I know. I shouldn't have. I do apologise.'

He snorted.

'This morning there will be another performance at the Temple of Hope,' he said. 'I trust that you will be able to make it. Miss Françoise will pick you up at the north entrance at the same time.'

'I wouldn't mind making my own way over there this time, if it's OK.'

'Miss Françoise will pick you up again at the north entrance at the same time.'

'Is that absolutely necessary?' I asked.

'Yes, sir, I believe it is,' he replied. 'Especially in the light of your little escapade yesterday. We look forward to seeing you again at the performance.'

'Any news on the break-in?' I asked.

'Managed to get that out of the girl, did you, sir?'

And with that he was gone.

I wandered up to the window with a glass of fresh orange juice again.

Someone was out there, over by the trees in front of the church. It must have been one of the gardeners. He was digging a deep hole – so deep that you couldn't see him. He was inside it and all that was visible was the spade that rose rhythmically into the air, again and again, scattering showers of earth on to the ground.

Françoise, back in her shades, was chatty in the car. I asked her if she'd heard about the break-in.

'Gosh,' she said, 'no, I haven't. What on earth happened?'

'I'm not sure,' I said. 'It happened last night, but that's all I know.'

'Well,' she said, 'I'm sure the boys will have dealt with it. They're very good at that sort of thing.'

'The boys?' I asked.

She laughed. Then she turned to me, grinning like a skull. I couldn't see anything in her face because of her sunglasses – great black suns devouring her eyes.

She looked ahead of her again.

'I call them that,' she said. 'But of course they're all grown men. Luke's men. Security – you know? Whenever I see them they always seem to be about to do something, to move from one place to another, from one job to the next. It's really quite exhilarating. They're alert, their chins and necks stick out, they stand with their hands on their hips, their guns hanging from their waists. I feel so safe with them around.'

'Where do you see them?' I asked. I had encountered one yesterday, of course, but he was the first. She made it sound as though they were everywhere.

'Oh, you know, when I'm driving around. They always give me a sharp salute. "Yes, ma'am," they say to me as they snap to attention. Sometimes I ask them to do things they shouldn't. And then they wink.'

'Do you do a lot of driving around?' I asked.

'Oh yes,' she said. 'I go all over the estate. Here, there and everywhere. I always have. Sometimes I look up and see Luke standing at his window, arms behind his back, watching me. I give him a wave. Sometimes Catherine comes with me. But she worries about me. So we crawl around when she's in the car. It's no fun.'

'Are you two best buddies then?'

'As far as sisters can be!'

'You're sisters?'

'Didn't you know?'

'No…'

201

'Françoise?' I asked.

'Yes?'

'Were you and Catherine named after the Dorléac sisters?'

'Yes, that's it. Poor old Dad was a sucker for all those New Wave French movies.'

We had arrived back at the field. Everything looked as it had the day before. The technicians were all there, and the camera crew. I looked up towards the stage. There were the Kid and the Killer, on their own again. The Kid had gelled his hair and it stuck up from his head in a dark wave. The Killer's face mask had gone now. Instead, he sucked on a thin rubber tube that led from his mouth down to a gas canister strapped to his belt. It looked as if he was carrying his own fire extinguisher around with him – ready to put himself out if he spontaneously combusted.

Haines was chatting to the director again, who this time was wearing a camouflage jacket, and shades pushed back on his head. Haines was wearing a strange costume, divided down the middle – on one side he was an office worker in suit, white shirt and black tie, on the other a Victorian street urchin.

Françoise had wandered off again. I walked towards the row of seats. There was no one there. It looked as though yesterday's pattern was going to be repeated. Once again I would be the only member of the audience. The props from yesterday had all been removed. At the back of the stage the white backdrop was still there, though. Now that it was more clearly visible, I could see that it was actually a huge cinema screen. In front of it now there was just a lectern with a reading light glowing a tiny yellow at the top, and a microphone stand.

I sat in the same place as yesterday. The screen was like the newly unfurled mainsail of a clipper ship. Against it the lectern looked insignificant, the microphone stand wiry and insubstantial.

I looked behind me. As before, the numbers there had thinned out. It wouldn't be long before the cameraman was the only one left again. Haines was by the steps. He had his scratched and beaten Gibson SG in his hand. Suddenly music began to pump from the p.a. – it was the beginning of 'Rock'n'Roll

202

Communiqué No.1', the opening track of *The Oliver Twist Manifesto*. He hoisted the guitar around his neck and bounded up the steps. With that divided costume, he would be two men up there this time. The stage was as empty around him as the arena was around me.

The music belted out from the hidden speakers and billowed across the field behind me.

Haines reached the microphone in perfect time for the song's first words – announcing itself as a non-entertainment, making a declaration of war on popular culture.

With his music pounding in my ears and his eyes boring into mine, it occurred to me that he was focusing all his contempt for that culture on to me. That he was imagining me as the epitome of all that he hated. Something flashed for a split-second across the huge blank screen, a subliminal image – of a B52 bomber.

After that, with a pause only to put down his guitar – which he hadn't played – it was straight into the next song, 'Oliver Twist'. And now the screen came fully to life. As Haines sang, the massive canvas behind him was filled with images of kids walking along Oxford Street, infiltrating the crowds and filling their pockets. Then there were shots of the Groucho Club and the Connolly Room, Soho House and the Columbia Hotel. Their doors were daubed with blood and offal. And then followed a sequence following Twist as he became airborne above a fog-drenched London before swooping down over Soho and closing in on the figure of Sarah Lucas smoking a cigarette outside a café. As the song ended, the screen froze on Twist taking aim at the Young British Artist with a water pistol.

'Is that "art"?' shouted Haines as the music faded, his words echoing around the stage and funnelling out across the field behind me. Then he looked at me again.

'Is what you do "writing"?' he said.

Then the music was suddenly cut. The final chord echoed around the stage for a second before I heard the sound of a single pair of hands clapping behind me and a shout of: 'OK, that'll do nicely. Like it, Luke, like it. Good one, mate.'

The clapping continued and came closer. I turned round to see the director walking towards the front of the stage. When he got there, Haines bent down to him and seized his hand.

'How was I?' Haines shouted as he walked towards the side of the stage, heading for the steps.

'Magic,' said the director, moving round to meet him again, 'I love it. You were buzzing.'

'Are we all set?' asked Haines.

'Everything's ready,' said the director.

'Then let's go,' said Haines.

And then Françoise was next to me again and taking me by the arm. And off we went – towards the Temple of Hope.

On the far side of the screen I was surprised to find that there were people milling around. There were about forty of them, crowded on to a patch of grass that was already becoming littered with cigarette ends and plastic wine glasses. Casual/smart was the dress code. They were mainly in their late twenties or early thirties, with a smattering of older men and a couple of well-preserved forty-something women. There was a babble of conversation, an air of mild expectation. A couple of them looked over at Françoise. When she nodded they began to move up the steps, past a large canvas on an easel, on which was painted 'The Strange Case of Christie Malry and the Oliver Twist Manifesto'. Once they'd started going in, the others joined them. Soon we were the only ones left outside. Françoise stepped forward and I followed.

Inside the front door we had to wait – the corridor was still full of people. Excited chatter now and shuffling feet. It was gloomy inside. A woman in a luminous white dress stood out, but the rest were a grey mass.

Finally we were inside a long, windowless, rectangular room. The walls – around which flat-screen television monitors were mounted at regular intervals – were white, as were the ceiling and the stone floor. Two men with shoulder-mounted cameras were mingling with the crowd. There was a table in the corner with neat rows of wine glasses, all filled to exactly the same height with champagne. Françoise went over and came back with drinks for us. She took us to the front of the room where there was a raised platform. We were near the girl in the white dress. Françoise caught her eye and she came over to us.

'This is Tamara,' Françoise said to me and then she introduced me, saying that I was writing a book on Haines.

'Oh, how marvellous!' said Tamara. 'Gosh, how interesting. He's so talented, isn't he – right up there with Damon and Noel.'

Before I had a chance to reply, a hush descended on the room. A metallic winching sound came from in front of us. A large trapdoor was opening on the platform. From the gap there, a wide flat-screen television monitor was rising up. It sat there for a moment and then – as we heard Haines's song 'Never Work' start up – it flickered into life.

As the song played and an invisible Haines urged the audience towards a general strike and a life of 'drifting', we watched a succession of film snippets and stills: Guy Debord in a Paris café, surrounded by acolytes, students on the streets of the Left Bank in 1968, the riots and the occupation of the Sorbonne – all punctuated by Lettrist and Situationist graphics, diagrams and maps. The members of the audience murmured to each other through their champagne.

As the music to the next song – 'How to Hate the Working Classes' from Haines's film soundtrack *Christie Malry's Own Double Entry* – struck up, Haines himself appeared from somewhere behind me and strolled on to the platform, taking up a position next to the TV. There were cheers, applause and a few shouts of 'Rock and roll!' and 'Rich bastard!', all of which he good-humouredly acknowledged. He had a dummy under one arm. It had a grease-stained face and dirty overalls. Holding it in front of him, Haines began to sing to it, offering it a part in a new political party based on hate. As the song's account of the developing mind-set of a terrorist ran its course, the screen filled with images of dole queues in the thirties, Oswald Mosley leading his Blackshirts down Brick Lane, German bombers flying over London, Harold Wilson, Ted Heath and the Kray Twins. When the song faded out, a fanfare blew – and then the National Anthem struck up. There were loud cheers around me. Haines took a handkerchief from his pocket and wiped a tear from the dummy's eye while, high up at the back of the room, a flag unfurled. It was a Union Jack, with a cut-out section filled with a photo of a happily smiling Haines. More cheers. Then as 'God Save the Queen' became his own 'England Scotland and Wales', Haines hurled the dummy – at me. I put up an arm to fend it off and it dropped lifelessly at my feet. There were a few gasps and several titters from the audience.

As Haines sang about writing his own national anthem, a section of the screen filled with an image of Winston Churchill, then a photograph of George Orwell appeared next to it, and finally, on the right of the screen, there was one of Lord Beaverbrook. Once they were all there, a message in thick red stencil-script emerged, letter by letter, across the trio: "Cell of one". As the music began to fade, Haines began an a cappella rendition of the first verse of 'Jerusalem' while behind him the screen showed an image of a baby-faced William Blake. Then Haines shouted, 'Art will save the world!' At that, the screens spaced around the walls of the room all came to life, each framing a glowing example of nineties Britart. There was a resounding cheer as the familiar Hirsts, Emins and Whitereads appeared. Suddenly next to me was one of the cameramen. And in front of me stepped a man with a microphone – the actor who had played Hitler and Edward VIII.

'And here we are,' he said, 'with the man who is currently writing a book on the man himself, Mr Luke Haines. What do you reckon to it so far, mate?'

Mate? I was furious. The guy didn't even know my name. I knew I had to come up with something that wouldn't make me look stupid, though – that much was clear in my mind.

'It's great,' I said, 'flashy, furious and fun.'

'Nice one,' he said. 'And what about that special moment when Luke brought you right into the thick of it?'

I had to pause a second for that one.

'Memorable,' I said.

'Yeah, a great moment for you, I'm sure. Cheers, mate, enjoy the show,' the actor said before darting away to greet a blonde in a blue dress.

A synthesised treatment of 'In the Bleak Midwinter' began to wash from the hidden speakers. The slogan 'Art will save the world', in thick red letters, filled the screen on the stage. As a choir started to sing the old hymn, Haines began to intone his own contradictory version set in Britain's cultural midwinter. The screens on the walls had now been transformed into a series of electronic stained glass windows. As the hymn and song continued, wrapped around each other, the screens turned, one by one, into flames until by the end it felt as though we were imprisoned inside a building surrounded by a wall of fire. On the screen next to Haines, photos of Hirst's formaldehyde animals appeared, along with Marcus Harvey's *Myra* and what seemed to be a bucket of piss – all ringed with fire.

As 'In the Bleak Midwinter' segued into 'Christ', Françoise reappeared next to me. I hadn't noticed that she had gone. She had brought a couple of refills. I grabbed mine gratefully and downed it in one. She took it from me and gave me hers – and I drank that, too. Then the screen split down the middle – the left half became black, the right white. As Haines sang his tale of contemporary iconoclasm, the black and the white began to dissolve into each other. Halfway through, all that was left was a grey that had spread across the whole screen like a fog. Against it, faint black and white photos appeared: of Duchamp and his urinal, Cage and one of his scores, Warhol and one of his electric chairs. Then, flitting across those, came colour photos of Haines in a variety of disguises – as Oliver Twist and Christie Malry, but also long-haired and leaning on a walking stick, in Louis Quatorze finery, in army fatigues and staring out to sea at Beachy Head.

Behind me I heard a commotion and then a couple of screams and then I felt a shove against my back. I turned round to see a short figure cutting a swath through the crowd – it was the Kid. He had a cigar in his mouth and a gun in his hand. People were getting out of his way pretty smartly. He forced himself past me and up to the platform where he handed the gun to Haines. Haines ruffled his hair and the crowd parted again so that the Kid, leaping off the stage now, could make his way back out. The intro to 'Mr and Mrs Solanas' had already begun and the image of Warhol's electric chair had stayed on the screen. Then it became duplicated again and again at different angles so that it looked as though electric chairs were tumbling across the screen. And then, as Haines sang his description of Warhol's shooting, another photograph appeared of the artist. Here he was holding up his shirt to expose the scars from Valerie Solanas's bullets. As Haines sang his story of wedding Solanas, what looked like a home movie was projected on to the screen behind him. Haines played a much older Warhol – first of all in a hospital bed, eyes closed, with tubes feeding in and out of his body, then lying on a mortician's bed, his face being powdered and made up, and finally in an open coffin. In each of the three sequences, the camera moved around the artist, examining him from above, below and the side. Cut into them were stills from the seventies and eighties – Warhol at Studio 54, on his own TV show and in the company of various showbiz celebrities. The song ended with a shot of one of his late-seventies piss paintings which, as the music to 'I Shot Sarah Lucas' began to emerge from the speakers, faded into a photograph of Lucas's yellow-resin toilet, *The Old In Out*.

Behind Haines as he sang now and toyed with the gun, an animated cartoon played: Haines opening a letter addressed to 'Mr Solanas' and taking out an invitation to a Lucas show; Haines at the typewriter bashing out a manifesto for SCUBA – the 'Society for Cutting up British Artists'; Haines walking into the show with a gun tucked into his belt – the same gun as the one he had in his hand now; Lucas in the gallery – which was this room – wineglass in hand; Haines taking aim and firing. But then, instead of the cartoon Haines firing, the real one took aim into the crowd and pulled the trigger. There was a loud bang, a few screams and then a grin from Haines to reassure the frightened guests. Behind him, his cartoon avatar strode out of the gallery and into the sunset.

And then a huge disco ball was lowered from the roof above the platform, the television monitor sank back into the floor and the trapdoor closed. White lights at the side and back of the platform fired beams at the ball, covering it in electronic sequins. 'Discomaniax' was the song pumping out of the speakers now and Haines was performing a series of energetic dance moves, arms and legs like pistons that had escaped from their engine casings. From behind me, four female dancers in tiny silver costumes emerged and stepped across the stage. There they pirouetted and strutted to the music, flinging themselves around as if they were dancing for their lives – all with wide smiles clamped to their faces.

At the side of the stage, the Kid had reappeared, and was shaking to the music. He was amazing – like a rubber doll – his body bending and gyrating like crazy. Where the Kid was, the Killer had to be. I spotted him – he was on the other side of the stage, his body jerking and pumping, his rubber tube taped to his cheek – showing no signs of any ill-effects. On the screens around the room there were shots of the Haines semi in the grounds – of the room where the actor playing him had sung in front of the mirror – and then a series of stills from American advertisements – smiling kids and soccer mums, close-ups of carbonated drinks, chocolates and sweets. As the music became more frenetic and the dancers whirled faster, there was a dizzying montage sequence in which I saw Osama bin Laden, Donald Rumsfeld and members of the Angry Brigade and the Baader-Meinhof gang.

The music now was 'Discomania', the original version – attacking the takeover of English popular culture by American corporations and the complicity of British governments, holding up Raoul Vaneigem's *The Totality for the Kids* as a revolutionary manifesto. The dancers, sweat pouring from their bodies, their costumes moulded to their skin, gave it everything. As the song ended, they jumped off the platform and ran into the crowd. Haines was looking across to the other side of the stage – where the Killer was now struggling theatrically with a skinhead. With a well-aimed blow, the Killer sent him flying and he sprawled on the floor, where the audience picked him up and cheered and he grinned, grabbing a girl and kissing her on the lips. Haines picked up a brick from the stage in front of him and pretended to hurl it at the nearest TV screen, which 'shattered' noisily. His version of 'I Love the Sound of Breaking Glass' was billowing across the room now. The screens had all gone blank. The Kid approached the stage with Haines's guitar. Haines patted him on the head. Then he grabbed the instrument, plugged it in and began to produce a seething mass of dark noise. There were no visuals at all now, no dancers, no actors, no images, nothing. Just the concentration on Haines's face. When it was over there was applause, shouts, whoops and whistles and Haines held up his hand to stop it.

Once the noise had died down he asked:

'Is death the end? Any ideas? Come on, half you lot are dead already, you ought to know.'

There were cries of: 'Ask Noel' and: 'See you in hell, Luke'.

'Oh please…' said Haines. 'Cryogenic freezing. It's all the rage. The undead hanging around, un-living with us. They think they're waiting for a cure for death, we know an opportunity for a little spare-part surgery when we see it. Actually, some of us don't die, did you know that? We just have too much to do, too much to say. This one goes out to the Comte de Saint Germain.'

The room went completely dark. More screams. Longer screams. Shouts. Pushes. Shoving. The only thing I could see was the tiny red light from Haines's amplifier – a malevolent, bloody electric eye watching from the back of the stage. Françoise had grabbed my arm. Her nails were digging into me. Then a hole was suddenly ripped in the darkness by a large, ghostly image in the top left-hand corner of the room, which began to spread across the ceiling. It hung there like a giant luminous moth – a dark Victorian figure with a moon-white face, shrouded in a black cloak. And then the image vanished, the room went dark again and a second image appeared – in the opposite corner. This figure shone a luminous green. Bewigged and frock-coated, swollen-faced and gaunt, it seemed to be suspended in flight, its eyes staring up at the roof, as if looking for escape. There were more screams. Suddenly we were blinded by a fierce white spotlight shining from the back of the stage. People turned away, clutching their eyes. We couldn't see a thing. Then a voice boomed out from up on the ceiling just behind me:

'Let's hear it for the Count!'

I could feel both Françoise's hands holding on to me. Haines's 'The Spook Manifesto' began to play. The music was hammering against my skull. When I managed to open my eyes again, the stage lights were bright and the screens around the room were flashing on and off in a chain of images that circled the crowd, faster and faster: of druids, King Arthur, the Black Prince, Oliver Cromwell, John Dee, Casanova. The lines about deaths, hauntings, time travel and the past coming back to life flew with the projections around the white walls. Then people twisted and craned their heads to catch images of Victorian women drooling ectoplasm, hell-fire preachers, medicine men on carts, voodoo dolls, bodies writhing as witch doctors cast out demons, Rasputin and the Tsarina, David Koresh, James Jones and Charles Manson.

As 'The Spook Manifesto' segued into 'The Oliver Twist Manifesto', there was a ruckus at the back of the room. I turned round to see that the doors there had been flung open. A horde of kids dressed as urchins, faces blackened, were running through the crowd, which was splitting apart, shrinking back, screaming and yelping. The kids pinched bottoms, ruffled clothing and grabbed handbags while Haines, as he sang, looked down like a proud Fagin. Once the kids had fully infiltrated the room, a shout went up from their midst and they began to move back again towards the doors, like a wave retreating. A few of the men aimed punches and kicks but the kids, whooping and hollering, dodged them and aimed a few back, most of which hit their mark. The women scrambled for the handbags that the kids hurled behind them as they left.

By the time they had all gone and the doors had slammed shut behind them, the ceiling was filled with a huge still of Richard Attenborough in *10 Rillington Place*, while on the screens around the room there were shots of him playing Pinky in *Brighton Rock* and Billy in *Seance on a Wet Afternoon*. Then, as Haines moved on to a description of the ghostly Twist emerging from the London fog, the room began to fill with dry ice. Spraying from all four corners of the room, it spread through the crowd, separating boyfriend from girlfriend, mate from mate, and setting them against each other as they collided, shouting in fear and anger. As Haines celebrated Christie coming back to life, some of them were actually on their knees, holding on to one another. When the Killer leapt from the stage, face luminous, coat full of lights, hammer drill whirling in his hand, and began to rampage through the crowd, it was too much for some. The stampede for the exit as Haines wrapped up the song and the doors were flung open again, a white cloud pouring through the open space into the corridor, was something to behold. The Killer chased them out, drill raised, unholy noises coming from his throat, and I was taken back to the night when I'd seen the X-Boogie Men stamping through the grounds.

I had dragged Françoise over to the wall, where we could watch the chaos without being caught up in it. I'd managed to grab a bottle of champagne from the table in the corner before it was shoved over. She snatched it from me now, lifted it and swallowed hard, liquid spraying from her grinning mouth. There was broken glass and champagne all over the floor – like miniature icebergs in a frothing sea. Then the dry ice was turned off and almost immediately the air began to clear. Most people were already outside. Of those that were left, men comforted girls or laughed with one another, punching shoulders in after-the-fact bravado. I saw Haines, a towel round his shoulders like a boxer after a bout, disappear through a door in the wall behind the stage.

Françoise and I wandered back outside. There was a coach there and the members of the crowd were filing on to it. A man who looked like a tour rep was shepherding them along. Most of the girls seemed to have recovered a little now, although some were still teary-eyed. They were smiling and beginning to chat. Some had their arms round each other. The men were becoming more boisterous, but suited security guards dealt with any that threatened to get out of hand, pushing them back into line. As the guests climbed on board, a man in a suit smiled and handed out £50 notes. We passed the coach – there were noses pressed against the windows and palms banging dully on the glass – and carried on to Françoise's car.

She sang tunelessly all the way back – maybe she had been deafened by Haines's performance. She was grinning again, too, as we flew across the fields.

Finally the car screamed to a halt outside the Hall.

I climbed out and looked back at her – dark-glassed and smiling, her left hand across the seat I had just left. Then she was off, wheels spinning and hair streaming.

Back in time for supper. I wonder what Henri has come up with tonight?

I'm back in my room.

I don't know what I've just eaten, but it was shit. Some kind of casserole with a sauce that tasted of beer. I did check with Stevenson – he said he was sure it was 'solid vegetarian fare'. But there was the definite flavour of animal flesh somewhere in there. The vegetables were a pile of soggy cabbage and a handful of barely boiled potatoes. Apparently Henri has been sent home temporarily. Stevenson claimed to know nothing of the details. As an emergency measure, one of the gardeners has taken over from him. Stevenson assured me that my supper contained mushrooms but the shrivelled grey things I was eating tasted and looked more like chopped up slugs.

While Stevenson was serving he told me that the story of the break-in had been a false alarm.

'Old Lionel, sir,' he said, 'is getting to be both rather clumsy and muddle-headed. Yesterday afternoon he managed to poke his hoe through the scullery window. In his frantic search for a dustpan with which to clear up the glass, he made quite a mess in there. Moving on in his search to the kitchens, he happened across a bottle of Henri's cooking sherry. By the time he stumbled off home an hour later, he had forgotten all about the broken window. When Donald saw the scullery door open and walked in to see the glass on the floor, the broken window and the state of the room, he leapt to the wrong conclusion. When the contrite Lionel appeared in front of me bright and early this morning, cap in hand, all became clear.'

'Oh, right,' I said. 'Not the kind of thing that would have happened in your father's day, I suppose?'

'Oh, all manner of unsavoury incidents used to occur back then, sir. It was just that they never became publicly aired. Father was a master at keeping these things under wraps. I blame television, sir. Reality TV, soap opera and documentaries about minor celebrities. They combine to define the world by gossip and rumour.'

I've finished writing up today's events. Time to crash out. Tomorrow must be Baader Meinhof day.

Editor's note—

I have decided to write today's commentary backwards. It seems kinder. The writer's final words tonight have such an air of foreboding. This way, we will leave him in good heart.

First, though I must say how pleased I was to find, appended to today's account by the writer, another message from 'Klaus'. I was starting to worry that we would never hear from him again! Welcome back, Herr Wolf, you cartoon German you!

Let me waste no more time in relaying his words:

'Guten abend.

I will inform you quickly of something you will want to know. I have to leave this place before morning. I have many things to do before then.

Luke had a great wish to perform his *Baader Meinhof* album in Berlin. He wanted local musicians who will play what he wanted with commitment. I found him such men – and a woman. He wanted, too, that he could play this music, so schön to him and to me and to friends of mine, to an audience containing these friends. I arranged this for him. He came to Berlin in a hired car and played for one day a rehearsal in a disused factory in Shöneberg. Later my friends arrived, one by one. Some were delivered in cars, some rode motorbikes, some had taken buses across the city or walked. Some of these friends travelled far. Older men and a few women. Most do not smile easily these modern days but they did so when they saw the big Baader-Meinhof poster at the rear of the stage.

I had more friends – different, younger ones – who came, too, and these friends were in the warehouse all day, watching at doorways and windows, concealing their AK47s and M16s. We had barrels of beer in the warehouse and a tape machine to play old recordings of Red Army Faction – Andreas and Gudrun and Ulrike and many more. We soon created a very good atmosphere. It was very noisy, there was much shouting and banging of beer mugs on our wooden tables – some having piles of magazines and books and tapes on their tops. At nine o'clock exactly, Luke and the band walked on to the stage. There was a roar from the assembled kamerads. Luke was, I think, nervous (he says no to this now). He walked slowly to the microphone, let his eyes move across the faces in front of him and said 'Guten abend, meinen herren und damen.' There was much applause and Luke smiled. The band began to play. They brought back to life the RAF.

Luke sang the songs of borders and airports and cops and bombs and my friends smiled. Some sang the words together with him. This record is a big cult album for them. It is not just the words – my friends like the music as well. They are 'sing-along' tunes with the beat of the Devil. My friends stamped their feet on the floor and clapped their hands. When Luke asked if they remembered Petra Schelm, many of my friends shouted 'Ja! Ja!' Some of them had tears in their eyes – Petra was our little sister, only 18 when she was murdered by our police state – and some put their arms around their women. When Luke talked in the same song about driving around on vodka and aspirin there were cheers of recognition. My friends remembered themselves. Luke's performance gave us an emotional evening. We were reliving a lost dream. When he sang about Carlos the Jackal and how we should kill 'el pirata corfisi' many of my friends spat on the floor. Yes, the floor was full of spit after that song.

During the final song there was much noise at the back of

the hall. Then we heard gunshots. Luke and the band stopped playing. My other friends shouted to us that we must leave. The warehouse is part of lots of buildings like a rabbit-house but we knew how to escape. My friends grabbed their ladies, and some pulled handguns from inside their jackets. With true socialist politeness they signalled to the musicians to leave first and then followed Luke and the band members at a fast pace. We heard maybe two or three more shots – no more – before we were out of there. We moved down more corridors, between walls and under the ground. Finally we were outside. Our two trucks were there, old Wehrmacht ones. We jumped into these and we drove away. We escaped. My other friends, the ones who protected us – one of them was wounded on this evening. He could not move. We picked him up, two of us, but he was in too much pain, there was too much blood. His guts were coming out of him. We laid him down on the floor as the kamerads gave covering fire. 'Shoot me,' he said. I was honoured to be the one who did it. We saluted him and we left. All others escaped with their lives – and their freedom. We do not live to become slaves. We live in freedom or we die.

'This evening was our final evening of remembering together. We had a big risk to be there – and Luke had that risk, too. He is a brave man and we also salute him. I have a videotape of the performance. It is one of my prize possessions. Along with Andreas's diary, Petra's blood-stained shirt and a lock of Gudrun's hair. Maybe one day I will show it to you.

'I must go. I hope to bring you more stories about Luke soon. Now, though, you must wish me luck. I must leave quickly.

Auf wiedersehen, kamerad. Alles gut. Heil Baader-Meinhof.

Klaus.'

What are we to make of this ludicrous story – whoever wrote it – which the writer presents to us, apparently signed by 'Klaus Wolf'? We may see misinterpretation, or we may see wish fulfilment, or we may see misrepresentation. Or perhaps we see all of these things? But maybe we just see mischief making, of one kind or another? Hang on a minute, though.

A bizarre thought has just occurred to me. *Perhaps the writer records this message here because he has somehow convinced himself that there is actually some truth in it?* For fuck's sake! Is he a child? Well – whatever. What he believes is of no importance to us. Although how it affects his mental state – and perhaps this is the important issue here – most assuredly does. Anyway, we move on to *Baader Meinhof* itself. Arguably, Mr Haines's best record.

I believe so.

The record was made in the summer of 1996 – football, Oasis, Tony Blair in the wings, touching up his make-up. It shows murder, violence, extremism and betrayal, all from inside the mind of a terrorist. It is an album that allowed Mr Haines to express his rage through the voice of a man defiantly outside society. Nihilism, the gang as a band, the gang as football hooligans, rich kids with guns. The end of the sixties, drugs and violence. Families and weak blood, love on the run – it is all there. The album appears to be 'by' the Baader-Meinhof gang itself. A terrorist group with a record contract. Why not? Their portraits are on the front cover. Inside the lyric book you will see more photos of the gang members, along with those of the PLO's Leila Khaled, Carlos the Jackal – and Mr Haines. The songs are about the gang, from the perspective of one of its members. All except for one, which features Mr Haines stepping outside the theatre of operations to berate his record company for not allowing him complete artistic freedom on the project. He had wanted the band to be called 'This is the Hate Socialist Collective'. They drew the line there for some reason. Its sound is a mixture of harsh seventies funk – Blaxploitation flavour – tablas and distorted guitars. Afro-America, India and England. A multicultural blend. It works perfectly. However, a 'concept album' about terrorism was unlikely to set the charts on fire – and so it proved.

'I'd still like to do a *Baader Meinhof* follow-up,' Mr Haines informed me during our chat. When the time is right, obviously.

He also told me that he once met ex-gang member Astrid

Proll at a 'horrible, trendy' event in a gallery deep in the enemy territory of Britart's London stronghold, Hoxton. The occasion was the publication of Ms Proll's nostalgic book of old BM photos. Here she refused to have her photograph taken with the only man in the field of rock and roll to have shed true artistic light – using such a large canvas – on the gang's life and times. She seemed, Mr Haines remembers, to be 'deeply confused' about her role in the events she was commemorating. Her denials of what she did have not helped her, he believes. 'You were involved in it,' he says. 'Get over it. People don't mind that you were. You're having your photographs shown in exhibitions, you're doing OK.'

Mr Haines managed to acquire a copy of her book at this event. I informed him that it now sells for hundreds of pounds. 'My book's signed by her so it's probably worth less,' he rejoined.

And so back to the writer. His last meal? Snails from the garden cooked in a mixture of centrifuged goat's blood and the purest of Austrian lagers. The food of the gods! It was good that this condemned man was able to eat so well if, sadly, not heartily.

Henri had to go. Fraternising with the enemy. Caught on film. In a less enlightened environment it would have meant death.

And so to Mr Haines's first appearance in person! Welcome, sir!

It is a shame that 'Tamara' overplayed her role (I believe that words were spoken afterwards), but the writer appears not to have noticed.

What the writer describes as a 'succession of film snippets and stills' that accompany Mr Haines's song 'Never Work' is in fact a tightly sequenced montage presenting a complex dialectical discourse about the role of work in a capitalist society. But never mind. Viewers of Mr Haines's film will be able to see it in full and to experience the full force of its political message unmediated by the writer's vapid ignorance.

In Lovecraft's 'The Case of Charles Dexter Ward', the deeply scary Dr Allen has '... a remarkable spiritual rapport with certain souls from the past…' Ward is summoned back to a previous era in order to raise his ancestor Curwen from the dead. Maybe Saint Germain, who appears on the ceiling of the room during the performance of 'The Spook Manifesto', has summoned Mr Haines for a similar reason – to facilitate his own further renewal? Saint Germain was rumoured to have discovered the secret of eternal life. 'Some of us don't die,' says Mr Haines. Saint Germain was rumoured to possess the secret of transmutation, the art of alchemy. Charles Dexter Ward's private quarters consisted of a bedroom, a library and an alchemist's laboratory. What, I wonder, is through that leather-backed door in Mr Haines's lounge?

During my delightful conversation with Mr Haines, I asked him whether the life of a one-man terrorist cell appealed to him.

'Any life lived outside the day-to-day that then becomes day-to-day is of interest,' he replied. 'Whether that is a fake spiritualist from Acton or a crypto-fascist from Bexhill-on-Sea. Good or bad, I am there.'

The writer used to live in Acton – in west London. His name and old address are in the front of one of the books in his room. Mr Haines has attended spiritualist meetings in this part of the capital. 'Although most of the attendees are clearly mad,' he remarked to me, 'I like the idea of people thinking they have some communication with a long-deceased loved one.' Mr Haines's grandmother on his father's side, he tells me, used to be quite active in the spiritualist church. Lionel Bart, writer of *Oliver!*, lived in a flat behind Acton High Street where, forgotten, he drank in order that he, too, might forget. In *Seance on a Wet Afternoon*, Billy, on his way to collect the ransom, stands in front of a sign pointing the way to the New Theatre in St Martin's Lane, where *Oliver!* was still on its triumphant initial run. Did the writer, too, attend spiritualist meetings in Acton, in search of the voice of his long-dead sister? I am with Mr Haines. I, too, like the idea of people thinking that they have some communication with a long-deceased loved one. It can create a path for them through sorrowful terrain. And, in rare cases, that path can lead to a new, mysterious place where closer contact seems to beckon.

The writer sees himself as the focal point of Mr Haines's anger at the state of popular culture. Well, all anger must be directed and, like a river, it finds its own level.

Mr Haines is dressed for his performance as the protagonists of his two 1998 solo albums, *Christie Malry's Own Double Entry* and *The Oliver Twist Manifesto*. One is a terrorist, the other a revolutionary. The title of the latter comes from an Angry Brigade missive. This pair of albums were a 1-2 in the flaccid face of the New Labour status quo. Mr Haines, when asked what had happened to the Auteurs now that he had 'gone solo', replied:

'The Auteurs have become Luke Haines. I ate their bodies, spat out their pips and sucked up their souls.'

Did Mr Haines anticipate the 9/11 attacks on *Christie Malry* and *Oliver Twist*? Who exactly are his 'kids from the base'? What exactly do they want?

When he presented *Oliver Twist* at the ICA in London on election night 2001, he was accompanied by a band of droogs. Inside the booklet for this album, Mr Haines is a pin-striped anarchist, a violent Magritte-man. There is a list of names in there. The album's sub-title is *What's Wrong with Popular Culture* – and these are the suspects. The booklet's photographs of Mr Haines fade to black. A dark strip has been taped across his nose. Inside the *Malry* booklet Mr Haines is at the typewriter, typing up another list – of those who owe him. They are in the 'debit' column – like the one Malry uses to fuel his terrorism. On the front of the album Mr Haines holds a placard saying 'Art Will Save the World'.

The kiddy pickpockets who terrorise the audience are on the cover of *Oliver Twist*, with Mr Haines as the Artful Dodger.

Miss Françoise chose her own roles. She was assured within them – stealing a baby, joining a terrorist group. There was never much she needed to do in the way of rehearsal. Even the lines that she learnt, assisted by a series of 'security personnel' in one of her lounges – the one in the arched lodge at which the writer was deposited by taxi at the start of this story – came easily to her. The poor young lady has had to live with the legacy of being named after a film star who died a tragic early death in a car crash. This has made her keen to ensure that the same fate does not befall her. This may partly explain the attraction to her of Mr Haines's imaginary armed men.

The break-in! Mary was in deep trouble over this, I can assure you. It would not surprise me if she had ended up over Stevenson's knee. It had been planned originally that a 'burglary' would occur. Various items would be removed, only to be found later underneath the writer's bed! The writer would declare his innocence, Stevenson would refuse to believe him, the writer would blame Mr Haines for framing him, etc., etc. The writer would feel more beleaguered, his confidence would be undermined and, most importantly, we would all have a jolly good laugh. Suggested during a rather raucous drinking session, it had seemed like a good idea at the time. Reconsidered from underneath the cloud of a dark hangover the next morning, it had looked a little infantile. For some reason, Mary seems to have got it into her pretty little head, though, that it was a goer. Fortunately, Stevenson managed to rescue the situation. Miss Françoise was able to use the story later as a way of introducing her intimidating but deeply fictitious security guards and, thanks to the writer's lack of imagination, that was that.

And so, yes, back to the writer. A double dose of Mary, first thing in the morning. How delightful. But how sad that he will never speak to her again. Still, I am glad that we are able to leave him today with a smile on his face. We, too, may smile as we think of him.

Day Nine

It was three o'clock this morning when they woke me. There was a bright light shining in my eyes. I thought I was back in that white room again, with ghosts on the ceiling, Haines's voice booming and the spotlight from the stage blinding me. All I remember then is the hands on my shoulders and chest, another hand clamped across my face, and then the chemical stink of chloroform filling my nose, throat and lungs. After that nothing – until I woke up in the back of a darkened truck, I don't know how many hours later, with moonlight cutting through tiny triangular gaps in the dark canvas.

We were driving across a bumpy road – it must have been the jolts that woke me. I was still very drowsy. I was lying on the floor and I was sore and bruised. My right arm was pinned under me – it felt as though I was lying on a joint of meat. My hands were numb, too, apart from a sharp pain around my wrists, which were handcuffed. Some kind of material was wedged between my teeth and knotted tightly around my head. I could feel it lodged into the skin at the back of my head, between two bones. On either side of me I could see dark military boots. Out of them grew legs in black, brown and green. I saw rifle butts, too, parallel with the legs, extending up to gloved fists. I didn't want anyone to know I was awake but I had to move because I was in so much pain. I shifted slightly, carefully, just enough to take the pressure off my arms and hands but even that tiny movement was enough to alert one of them. I was grabbed, yanked up and shoved on to a seat.

I felt a rich, glorious pain then as the blood began to return to my hands and my arm. As the sensation tore through my muscles, I gritted my teeth and tried to examine my companions. There were eight of them, sitting on wooden benches along both sides of the truck. Eight dark figures, faces blackened. I could tell, from their shape and size and the way that they carried their guns, that at least two of the figures on the seats were female. Apart from that, there was nothing to distinguish any of them. I tried to speak then through the gag but received a punch in the stomach for my trouble – strong enough to wind me. I doubled up, trying to gasp through the rag, my body heaving as I tried to seize air and force it in to my lungs.

I don't know how much longer we drove. I nodded off a couple of times before the pain from my bruises and the bumps on the road woke me again. None of the others in the truck spoke.

Eventually we stopped and then I heard a few whispers around me. I couldn't understand what they were saying – it was all in German. Then I heard the two doors at the front of the truck open and then close – carefully, quietly. And then the tarpaulin at the back of the vehicle was being hauled up.

Moonlight slanted in, a triangle of illumination which stretched from the doors at the back to a panel at the front that sealed off the driver's compartment. The light didn't help – all I saw were balaclava'd faces, camouflage jackets, more boots and trousered legs. I looked outside. We were in a small clearing in a wood. Then we began to get out – I was half-carried and half-shoved – and finally we were all standing in a group in the middle of the clearing – me struggling to stay upright after being handcuffed for so long. Behind the truck I could see the track we must have come down, vanishing into the trees.

One of the members of the group had a video camera. He took a few paces back and began to film us. Some of the others waved and began to gesticulate like monkeys – but without making a sound. It was like some crazy silent movie.

Then we began to move off, in single file, into the woods.

I stumbled several times. Brambles tore at my face. At one point I hissed 'Catherine!' to the girl up ahead – and got a rifle barrel in the ribs for my trouble. I had no idea where we were or where we were going. Back in the truck I had tried to concentrate on changes in terrain, sounds from outside – anything that might have given me a clue to my surroundings. All I had heard and felt, though, were the regular dip and surge of the diesel engine over the same bumps and ruts. Trying to get any idea of direction had been hopeless. We had made so many twists and turns that I was completely disorientated.

It was little different now that we were in the woods. With the figures in front of me blocking my view ahead and those behind preventing me from turning round – and nothing but thick trees on either side – I was as good as blind. All that my ears picked up was the tramping of boots on earth and the occasional soft hiss of 'Scheisser!' as one of those boots lost its footing. We snaked our way deeper and deeper into the woods – like rebel forces in the jungle. And I was their captive.

Eventually, between the heads of the figures in front of me, I saw that we were about to emerge from the woods into another clearing. Our pace slowed until we were barely moving. Then our leader stopped and held his hand up in the air.

He stood for what must have been at least a minute – looking and listening. The clearing ahead was much larger than the one where the truck was. There was a vast dark building dominating it.

Finally we began to file out of the woods, and fan round the edge of the clearing.

In front of us, set behind a barbed-wire fence and very black against the moonlit sky, was a massive warehouse. It was a similar size to the one where I had seen the light aircraft and watched the battle for its pilot's mind, but its shape was different – the roof sloped towards us and there was a canopied entrance in the middle. To my left, at what had been the head of the procession, I heard two of our company whispering – and heard the name 'Andreas'. Then the next two group members in the line crouched down and began to run towards the perimeter fence. The two immediately on my left, one male and one female, then broke away from us, too – he to the left, she to the right. The first pair reached the fence and sat on their haunches, working away at something. I caught the gleam of wire-cutters in the moonlight. Then, to my right, I heard a sound that whipped my head round. It was a stifled scream – followed by a muffled moan. The skin was taut on my face, my chest puffed and solid. In the pale glow I could just make out the silhouette of a man removing what seemed to be a gleaming knife from a prostrate figure. As I saw an arm lifted in triumph from the fence, I heard a fainter cry of pain, cut short again, from somewhere out of sight round the other side of the warehouse.

The rest of us began to follow then. I was dragged and pulled, and then hurled into the dirt as we reached the wire. One by one, we squeezed through the gap. When it was my turn I stuck my head and shoulders between the jagged ends, and the others yanked and shoved me through. The broken wire tore at my clothes and skin, scratching and ripping. I can see the scars, etched along my arms, as I write this. Evidence of what I did last night.

We ran again then, towards the main doors of the warehouse. Another member of the gang peeled off to the left. The rest of us stood there, panting, looking at one another. I still couldn't make out any detail on the faces. From her profile, one of the women could have been Françoise, but it was impossible to say, even though she was close to me. There was nothing about the way she moved or behaved that was like her.

The cameraman was pacing about, filming us. There was no more clowning around, though. Everyone was motionless as he prowled – not even heads turned to follow him. Then, from somewhere off to the left, we heard a dull boom – and the ground beneath our feet seemed to shiver. Andreas walked up to the door. He had a drill in his hand and began to work on the wood around the lock. Sparks flew when he hit metal. We all watched, hypnotised by the sound and the sawdust flying out like spent rocket fuel in the moonlight. Finally he pulled the drill away. For a second it whirred louder and then it stopped. Then he aimed a kick at the door and it lurched open.

The explosion hadn't been to get us in to the building – it had been to disable the alarm system. He moved inside and we followed him.

Once we were all in, Andreas closed the door and switched on the lights. They flickered a few times and then came on full. Dazzled, we blinked as they lit up what seemed to be a large, empty, white hall – like a mausoleum waiting for its first corpse. In fact, I saw as I looked around me, there were narrow staircases at each of its corners, moving diagonally up the walls. Halfway up they met four more staircases, which moved at right angles up to the second floor of the building. On each floor there were gantries that gave access to rows of half a dozen doors.

Andreas grabbed me by the arm and marched me towards one of the ground-floor doors. We were followed by the guy with the camera. When we stopped, Andreas reached into his pocket and took out a bunch of keys. I thought he was about to open the door but instead he grabbed my wrist and undid the handcuffs. Then he untied the gag. I rubbed my wrists and stretched my arms. I grimaced and began to work my jaw up and down, and round and round. There was no time to enjoy the feeling of blood and movement returning, though – Andreas was motioning me towards the door. It was slightly ajar, I noticed now. I looked along to the next one, and then down the line. They all were – they had slipped their latches. The explosion must have taken out the electronic locking. With the cameraman at my shoulder, I pushed open the door. Andreas's finger reached out in front of me. A light snapped on. I walked in, the cameraman following. The walls were full of artworks.

I didn't recognise all of them but the genre to which they belonged was obvious – this was Britart. There were Emin tapestries, Sarah Lucas self-portraits, the Chapman Brothers' vandalised Goyas, Hirst's psychedelic circles. Once I had done a circuit of the room, Andreas beckoned to me. We went out on to the walkway again and I was motioned towards the next door. Inside I could see what seemed to be a large box in the centre of the floor, and then Andreas hit the light switch and I saw that there were, in fact, two large containers – and they were actually tanks, made of glass. There were also two smaller ones. All the tanks were filled with a greenish liquid. Each, too, contained half a cow. This was Hirst's *Mother and Child*.

I was filmed staring at it and wandering around it for a minute or two and then the cameraman signalled me to leave – a middle finger that first pointed to the door and then up, at me. As I left he was lying on the floor, aiming the camera at the mother. Outside, Andreas pushed me towards the stairs.

As we reached the bottom, four of the other gang members spread out across the floor, each heading for a different staircase, each removing a shoulder bag and opening it as they went. As Andreas and I arrived back at the main door and turned to watch them, they were already moving along the gantries and opening doors. From their bags they had taken cans of petrol. Each began to move into the rooms and lay trails of fuel inside. We watched them as they moved from doorway to doorway, pausing only to remove reserve tanks from their bags when they needed them. Once they had finished, three of them reversed back along the walkways and then down the stairs, pouring petrol in their footsteps. When they reached the bottom, each began to trace a line back to us. At the end we were left standing a few feet from a shimmering pool of rainbow-coloured liquid. The smell of petrol was thick in the air. The cameraman had been filming all this, moving round the hall to capture all the action.

Then there was a shout from one of the galleries above. The cameraman brought his camera to bear just as the fourth gang member heaved a glass tank on to the balcony rail and shoved it over. It turned slowly as it fell, liquid leaving it in a fat wave of spray. An object flew out from it, too, and began to twist in the air – a half-animal had escaped from its glass cage and its half-life. It was gambolling, in its few brief seconds of freedom, through the empty space towards a second death. The tank hit the floor with a thud and a smash, and glass scattered across the floor, coming to rest in shallow, jagged puddles. Andreas, pulling on a pair of heavy duty gloves, marched over and grabbed the bedraggled half-animal – a goat – by its rear hoof. He had a knife in his hand. He walked back to us with it and stopped a couple of yards in front of me. He took the knife and slit the goat's half-throat, flicking the animal towards me. Impossibly, blood spurted from it, on to the floor and on to my feet. Then Andreas reached inside the flesh of the goat and tore something out. Ripping it apart, he flung its bloody contents at me. I fended them off with one hand, protecting my face with the other. The handful of guts landed at my feet. But there was no sting of formaldehyde on my skin. I looked down. The 'guts' were cloth bags dripping with red dye.

Then there was another shout from above. The fourth gang member was now holding a silver salver up in the air – and on it was a skull, covered in diamonds that flashed silver, blue and red across a thousand different planes. The cameraman swivelled upwards again and the gang member hurled the salver into the air. It fell away from the skull, which began to revolve like a misshapen disco ball as it fell, firing light chaotically into the air – and then there was a loud explosion from the gun in the upheld hand of Andreas and the skull shattered, sending shards of jewelled bone and a cascade of glittering, frozen raindrops through the air, which showered down and then scattered across the floor like hail.

Now the camera had swivelled back to earth. The lens was pointed firmly at me. As were the guns of the other gang members. Andreas handed me a plastic lighter. It was tiny, flimsy. I weighed it in my hand. It barely existed. Then I flicked my thumb, the flint grated and a flame rose from my finger. In here, now, this lighter was as powerful as a blowtorch or a flamethrower or an incendiary bomb. I bent down. I looked at the camera. 'This one's for you, Haines,' I said – and then I lit the fuse.

It raced along the ground like a small boy in the snow, then split into tributaries, then climbed, grinning, up the stairs. From there it skated along the gantries and tripped into the rooms – and when it got there it fed on itself, expanding, accelerating, intensifying.

Before long, every doorway was ringed with fire as black

smoke funnelled out through them and into the hall, and flew up to the ceiling. There it curled and furled, spreading across the whiteness and turning it red and black, racing for the walls, where it built and built before overflowing downwards to meet the fire coming up, and then combined with it to take over the available space with the speed of bacteria multiplying. And then it was colonising the air. The doorways were red and orange and almost shapeless, losing their form to that of the fire itself, which had assumed its full identity now – becoming something grander, more primitive, magical. It was like watching the sun burn.

Smoke was filling the hall. The edges of the terrorists were becoming blurred. They were like figures in an antechamber of hell. Andreas shouted a retreat and we made for the door. The cameraman was the last one out. He reversed out of the building, lens pointed, as if withdrawing from the presence of the Sun King.

Once we had all gone back a safe distance, we turned and watched. Fire was already licking the external walls of the building and smoke puffing gently through the open door. The warehouse looked like a red-haired giant, buried up to its neck, smoking a cigar. Over on the edge of the wood the cameraman prepared a long-shot.

No one had tried to put the cuffs back on me. They must have realised they didn't need to. I was as transfixed as the rest of them. And as culpable. More culpable in fact – I had lit the fuse. I had started all this. Now I was on the same side as these people, their cause was mine. If I ran, it would be into the arms of the enemy. Fire was spilling out from the building's sides now, beginning to envelop the walls. All that stuff inside burning, melting and disappearing, turning into nothing.

From somewhere – in English – I heard the words, 'Burn, warehouse, burn.' From someone else I heard 'Burn, *Hell*, burn.' And then someone else muttered, 'Again', and there were some guffaws. At its heart now the fire seemed white and solid.

We turned and began to head back. I moved smartly through the woods this time – moving freely now, clearer-headed, and knowing what to expect from the terrain. And I was buzzing. Excited about what we had done.

As we stood at the back of the truck again, I caught the whiff of chloroform once more and surrendered to the gloved hand. The last thing I remember is staring up into the tousled, dirty, unmasked face of Catherine.

When I woke up I was back in my room at the Hall.

For a moment, I seemed to see myself lying on the bed, as if I was looking on from the other side of the room – having some kind of out-of-body experience. Or as if there were two of me. It must have been the after-effects of the chloroform.

Once I'd come to properly and had a shower I decided to get some fresh air. On the way down, I could poke my nose into the kitchen and see what was for lunch. Yes, I was hungry again! The night was over – Haines had done his worst and I had survived it.

When I got downstairs there was no one around. And complete silence. I stood in the corridor for a moment, looking down the hall – the kitchens on the left, the dining hall to my right. No sound, no signs of life.

I walked into the kitchen. No pots on the worktops, no piles of vegetable peelings waiting for the bin, no heaps of ingredients ready for the pan. I went over to the massive stove with the twin ceramic doors – cream-coloured, they bulged out of their frame. It was cold. I walked across the kitchen and stared out of the windows that looked over the north side of the Hall. The sun was up high – it must be nearly midday. The kitchen should be buzzing with activity. I looked out at lawns, fences, fields, birds. But no people. Everything out there was neat and ordered. The gardeners must have been working hard – but now they were nowhere to be seen.

I turned round. Everything in the kitchen was massive. Huge freezer doors on my left, big enough to stand up in, the stove in front of me with those swollen oven doors, grilles like crematorium burners, and cobra-like extractor hoods. Over on the shelves were the soup tureens, the giant casserole tins and saucepans like plump warming-pans.

I went out of the kitchen and crossed the deserted corridor

into the dining hall. I stood there for a moment in the delicious chill of all that empty space. I had a sense of complete absence about this place now. Sometimes you can tell when there's no life in a building. And there was none here.

Back out in the corridor, I turned right into the marbled hall that leads to the south entrance and crossed the stone floor that was packed so solidly and evenly into the ancient earth below. And then I was standing in front of that tall, grand oak door, with its tiny copper handle that you had to stoop to turn. And then I opened it and once again I was on top of the steps, staring out at the rolling lawn, the lake and the distant arch.

I walked down the steps towards the expanse of carefully cultivated grass. It seemed to rise up to meet me. The Hall stretched behind and above me like a giant pair of my own dark wings.

I crossed the path on to the lawn. The gentle slope tugged at me, like a small child pulling at my sleeve, leading me towards the lake.

When I had got down there, I stopped on the edge of the water, as I had done before, and looked out over its bullrushes, bright marsh marigolds and lilies. The two swans were gliding there, necks curled – true aristocrats.

Then I walked again along the side of the lake, the water bright blue with sky, before stopping where the woods began and staring back up the slope towards the Hall. I looked at it afresh from here. It was as if, now that it was empty, it had been given the chance to express itself freely for the first time. I could almost see it stretching, hear it drawing in breath and exhaling with a huge, soft sigh.

On my left, hidden behind the trees, was the glass building where I had witnessed the confessions of Françoise and Catherine. At the top of the slope, the other side of the stone-covered path, was the granite building with the giant stone ball balanced on its roof. Tucked away to its right was the block where I had been given my school lesson. A breeze was starting to blow. I returned to the Hall.

Back in the kitchen, I began a more detailed search – I was scavenging for food. First up were the two walk-in fridges

– cold-stores with enough room to feed a wintering army. I heaved at one of the doors. The cold air inside rushed to escape. But it left nothing behind. The shelves were bare. The metal bars running across the fridge's ceiling were empty. There were no heavy, round cheeses or fat, square boxes of butters with their cardboard ends ripped off, no transparent, factory-sealed parcels of sickly paté. Not even a half-empty carton of milk past its sell-by date. The meat hooks hanging from the bars had been shoved neatly down to one end where they had gathered like a row of 'S's discarded from a child's alphabet. There were no sides of bacon hanging, no gutted pigs dangling from their pierced trotters with their ears flopping towards the floor – no blood and fat pooling there. I closed the door.

The freezers were no good to me – even if there was anything inside. Big, hard chunks of dead animals were all they ever contained. Underneath each of them were huge, slide-out drawer-compartments. One night I had opened a drawer and found the head of a deer inside.

Now I moved around the kitchen, opening cupboards and drawers, searching at the back of units and in corners. I found something in the end – some scraps for my belly. A couple of wholemeal crusts and a near-empty jar of peanut butter. I sat on the window ledge, rolling the bread up and shoving it into the jar, scraping the thin ruts of dry paste on to it.

Outside the wind was getting up. Clouds tracked across the sky, trees dipped, leaves shook like the zils on a tambourine. Dark birds made intricate patterns as they zigzagged and curved against the clouds. I sat there, staring. Waiting for a gardener to come into view, for a delivery truck to arrive, for Françoise to pull up, hair streaming in the breeze.

And then, finally, I got up. And went back along the corridor, past the entrance hall, past the drawing room and further on – towards the staircase leading to Haines's quarters.

The wall-to-wall carpet here was a deep dark red, the walls were covered with a biscuit-coloured silk damask, the edges of the skirting boards and the wooden rails above were neat and sharp. I turned and looked at the coat of arms as I passed – a couple of strange looking birds sitting on top of a globe. And then the corridor grew lighter and the carpet became white. The walls now were lined with a series of gilt-framed paintings of Italianate ruins, Renaissance gardens and picturesque harbours with old fishing boats. There was a different feel here – money and power were packed more tightly into these walls.

The carpet on the stairs up to Haines's rooms was thicker, hemmed in and pulled straight by gold stair rods. On the right as I climbed was a pair of wall-mounted candle-lights, like illuminated hands.

At the top I came to a landing. There was a table there with a bowl full of dried flowers – red, orange and gold – and sun-bleached corn.

Blocking the way to the next flight of stairs, though – the one that led, finally, to Haines's rooms – was a locked door. Dark, solid oak with a tiny keyhole. I rapped on it with my knuckles. The sound barely registered. The thick grain of the wood swallowed it whole. All that was visible of that higher staircase was a single step leading up to the door. I bent down and looked through the keyhole. But there was nothing there – just darkness. Even though the Hall was now deserted I was still only being allowed to see what Haines wanted me to see.

There was a small, heavily recessed window in the stone wall next to the door. The old church in the woods was just visible through it. I thought I saw something moving out there. For a minute or two I stood, staring through the trees. Until my eyes began to blur. Then I went back to my room.

It was only when I got back here that I noticed the piece of paper, half concealed by the clothes littering the floor, that must have been slid under my door some time before I woke up this morning. It was a message from Stevenson, of all people, handwritten and neatly folded in two, and it read:

'Good day to you, sir. I trust you have slept well. Mary and I have both been at your door this morning but neither of us have been able to raise you. We thought it best to let the sleeping dog lie! I have withdrawn to the Morning Room to write you this letter.

'Mr Haines is a good man. You will see that in the end, I believe. "Goodness" does not, of course, necessarily imply delicacy. He is a firm believer in the old adage that the end justifies the means. And when a saying has stayed in common parlance in a country, within a culture, on an island, for so long, it does acquire a permanent significance, do you not think? A truth that is inarguable.

'We all occupy our own space in the bigger picture. And that picture is a backdrop in the theatre within which we play. It only becomes truly visible once all the actors have been removed from the stage, from the wings, from the dressing rooms, from the very theatre itself. And even then, the viewer must stand back in order fully to appreciate it.

'We all have our ghosts, too, sir, do we not? Our ghosts that accompany us to our beds at night and stay with us while we sleep, and sometimes cause us to rise from those beds and to wander alone, far from them. We are all presented with things in our lives that we would rather not acknowledge but which force us, finally, to acknowledge them.

'I am sure that you remember me talking about my father. He did not choose his own path. You and I make our own mistakes and live with them, do we not? My father made his, that is true enough, but he lived with – and by – someone else's. He was not a good man. Not in the only way that matters. He was not violent, he was not selfish and he did his duty as it was defined for him. But he was not a good man because he did not have courage. For without courage we are nothing. My father went to war and fought, but he did not have courage. My father endured hardship and poverty, but he did not have courage. My father defended and worked for my mother, but he did not have courage. My father's actions were chosen for him. He never had the courage to question them – because he never had the courage to question those who had ordered them.

I hope that these ramblings may perhaps be of some use, somehow, to you.

With my very best wishes,

Sincerely yours,

Stevenson'.

Stevenson, it seems, is a good man – by my definition of the word, anyway.

And now it's late. And I'm writing this before I go out into the night. I think I can hear something outside. Yes – faintly on the wind. It sounds like fairground music. I must go. All being well, I'll be back by the end of the night for a couple of hours' sleep before I wake to the vision of Mary holding a steaming cup of tea. And then I will go downstairs to be greeted by Stevenson with a tray of toast and marmalade. And the smile of an old friend.

Editor's note —

Right. Very soon now we will join the writer on the final stage of his journey into reality. But first let us joyfully relive the events of last night! How fortunate we are to be able to push him through that experience again – to repeat his pain. And we will be able to season our review of those delicious hours with our own piquant anticipation of the unknown danger that still awaits him. A double delight!

The writer is in his sanctuary. He sleeps. See, though, how he is dragged from the shores of the Lethe by dark shades from the Styx. But see now how they take pity on him. With a single chloroformed hand to the mouth they return him to the land of forgetfulness.

Three cheers for the extent of Mr Haines's estate and its network of roughly maintained roads and tracks! The key to persuading the circumlocutory writer that he was travelling miles and miles from the Hall! The sequences filmed with the infra red camera in the back of the truck are some of the funniest in Mr Haines's film. A jolly good time was had by all while the actors waited for the writer to show signs of life, and Catherine could barely contain herself under her balaclava as they passed the Hall for the umpteenth time.

The issue of pain was discussed at length before today and it was finally agreed that it would be necessary to inflict some. Stevenson was opposed to this view – although his opinion was expressed with due decorum. Nevertheless, when the democratic vote went against him, he, of course, agreed to enforce it, and proceeded to shoulder responsibility in the way that we have come to expect from him.

It is unfortunate that the *scheisskopf* writer was unable to understand what was said in German – surely abuse, no matter how veiled or sardonic, should never need translation? And who said Germans had no sense of humour – or irony? Oh, I forgot – they're not German. They're English actors. They all played their many parts so well! English neofascist/German pseudomarxist – it's all the same for these guys. And the screams of the 'murdered' guards! I can almost feel the pain of the knives entering between their ribs.

The warehouse is, of course, the very same one at which the writer witnessed the conflagration inside the light aircraft. But viewed from the other side. In previous days it was used for storing the third Earl's huge collection of military memorabilia. His specialities were the Franco-Prussian War, the German colonisation of East and South West Africa and the early years of World War One.

It is good to see that the writer seems to have appreciated the art works inside the warehouse. It is amazing what you can do with a high-class photocopier and a 'wife' who likes knitting. The local butcher was most accommodating over the instructions for the cows and the goat. The calf, you will be pleased to hear, died of natural causes, while the aged goat, a family pet from a neighbouring farm, had been suffering from a badly swollen liver and was humanely slaughtered. Even the cow had lived longer than most – providing milk in pleasant conditions on said farm. I thought you might like to know these things. Obviously the other rooms were all empty – no sharks, sheep or flies, no cigarettes, unmade beds or wax soldiers. But they can still burn in our dreams.

Mr Haines was very happy to see the warehouse go up in flames – a little dressing up and it made for a superb burning down. A fine false climax to his film. The ghostly lungs of Bismarck's and the Kaiser's men screamed every bit as loud as the plastic ones of the Chapmans' toy Nazis do in our heads.

'Burn, warehouse, burn' were, of course, the final words of a pamphlet issued by the German revolutionary group Kommune 1 after a department store fire in Brussels in May 1967. The pamphlet warned of arson attacks against similar stores in Berlin in protest against the Vietnam war.

Catherine was amused to find that the writer saw a vision of her as he slipped into his second slumber. She tells me that she was, in fact, in the front of the truck when the chloroform was administered, indulging in some light-hearted banter with no less a person than 'Andreas Baader'. Surely she is not attempting to pull the wool over my eyes? Wait a minute – Catherine! Come here! Were you leaning over that scribbler on that forest floor? Were you attempting to comfort him? Come here immediately and accept your punishment like a lady!

The writer wakes to find himself possibly having 'some kind of out-of-body experience'. Or perhaps, he thinks, there are actually two of him? The latter sensation is common, apparently, among the siblingless. But I concur with him that, in his case, the phenomenon is isolated and most likely to have occurred as a result of his chloroforming. For, despite Jessica's death, he has never truly been without his sister – he has always been visited, at regular intervals, by her ghost. No, true doubling is the prerogative of the only child who really has no one to talk to.

Of course Mr Haines was reading the writer's electronic scribblings every night. Yes, they were useful to him, but not very. Even at the start, the writer seems not to have been entirely open with himself. And as his writing proceeded, his tongue even tightened. Mr Haines had been expecting a certain amount of good old-fashioned abuse, to spur him on, but sadly it was not forthcoming. No problem. There was plenty else to fuel his anger: stupidity, ignorance, a mild death wish, etc., etc. But there was one point, early on, when the writer did let himself go – and wrote something that made Mr Haines's eyes grow large as he read. I removed it from the writer's account. Not for the same reason that I drained the book of all the warbling about his poxy magazine and other bits and pieces of no interest – stuff about family, childhood etc. We do not want to know about how he made coffins for dead birds! No, I removed this particular passage because it had appeared in the wrong place. It should have been at the end of the book. That was where I wanted it to be and that is where it is. Here:

'Jessica died when I was five. She was three. There was a heavy fog that day. Thick, grey curtains flapping in the air. And they were wet, too, wrapping around my face, their moisture soaking in to my throat. The sun was like a moon. It was cold. We were down at the boating lake in the park. But there were no boats on the water. We had gone in our winter coats. Jessica was wearing white mittens, too, and a red hat that fastened under her chin. Mum had just finished tying up her shoelace, her hands still down by Jessica's feet, when we heard a scream from somewhere in the bushes behind. Mum stood then and turned and stared. I stared, too. We were both looking through the leaves and branches, into the fog, trying to see through it, searching for the person who was in danger. But Jennifer hadn't turned. Maybe she had heard something else. Maybe a moorhen calling out on the water. After the scream, Mum and I heard laughter from the bushes – it was just a couple of kids messing about. And then we turned back – but Jennifer had gone.

'We were standing next to the wooden platform that ran out into the water. The tight dark planks vanished in a sea of mist. I could just see the first of the boats tied up alongside – half a wooden rowing boat, half a wooden seat. Hints, perhaps, of an exciting new world. Mum shouted 'Jessica!' – anxious, but not too worried yet, expecting a call back, or a sight of her tiny figure toddling towards us, arms outstretched, with that wide smile on her face. But there was no sound from Jessica and no sign of her either. Mum grabbed me by the hand and ran with me on to the platform. Together, we ran into the fog. Mum was screaming. From now on, she didn't stop. She crouched down on her ankles, trying to look underneath the fog. I got down there with her and reached out, trying to push it away, to lift it up. And then came the sound of heavy feet and there were two men running along the platform towards us. Mum screamed at them: 'My daughter! My daughter,' and then they were pulling off their coats and shoes and jumping in. They went under the water and they came up again, splashing and inhaling and shouting at each other before they plunged back. Then they moved further out into the lake and further along the wooden platform. I lost one from sight. I saw the other's mouth reach up into the air and take a deep breath – but then he vanished in the fog. There were shouts and splashes for a long time and the noisy sound of surfacing and gulps for air and always Mum's steady screaming, but none of it was any good. It was the diver, much later, who found Jessica – not the police or the ambulance or any of the others who had come running. He found her on the bed of the lake. She had been dragged down by her coat and shoes and hat, and everything else that Mum had dressed her in to protect her from the cold and the fog. She looked very peaceful, they said. But I wasn't there then. I was back at our neighbour's house. The last I saw of my sister she was standing just in front of me, hands outstretched, smiling her three-year-old smile.'

The writer let this passage stand. At no point during what followed did he attempt to delete it. No, the writer, who has been guarded about much of his personal life, stood by what he had written here. Maybe he thought that he could use it to somehow engage with his sister's death, and then even to transcend it? And maybe Mr Haines, having read what he had written, was able, in his own way, to assist him in this? That would have been uncommonly decent of him.

It is good to see that the writer has come to terms so easily with the deaths of the two innocent security guards – good men with families to feed and mortgages to pay, no doubt.

The writer believes that he has survived Mr Haines's worst! The worst is always yet to come, dear writer, for a man like you.

Alone in the grounds of the Hall, the writer exhibits a bad case of 'melancholia in arcadia'. Sounds like the title of some dodgy prog-rock album. I suppose we must allow him his moment of voluptuous misery. It will be eradicated soon enough by a dose of the more vicious kind.

Why is the place deserted? Why are all the fridges empty?

Because when Mr Haines and company have finished watching the night's entertainment, relayed from the cameras in the grounds to the monitor screens in the old ballroom, they will dine in town. And after that they will be whisked away by limousine to a five-star hotel in the capital. From which, at their leisure, they will repair to warmer climes for a month. After which they will return for the post-production work. The gardeners? Standing around a trestle table at the rear of the ballroom, craning their necks for a good view of the screens, supping their home-made cider.

The mention of the deer in the freezer is interesting because it refers to a part of the writer's stay at the Hall that features nowhere else in his account. The writer had a habit of sneaking in to the kitchens after meals and chatting with Henri. Perhaps he believed that this *maître de cuisine*'s ability to concoct a delicious vegetable casserole somehow made him into a soul mate. Well, we will never know that and the writer will never know just how close he might have got to Henri. As previously mentioned, the conversations between the two were monitored. Once the writer began to seek help in 'getting out of here' – a request to which Henri bizarrely showed himself inclined to respond – the chef's hours at the Hall were numbered. The writer should have realised that, having chosen a solitary life, he would have to live it to the full.

The writer stands with his eye to the keyhole of that oaken door – but he sees nothing. Well, he would not. He was staring into a lens affixed to the dark interior of one of Mr Haines's cameras. The lens, on the other hand, had a very good sight of the writer's eye, with its twitching ball and lashes. It forms a striking image in Mr Haines's film, blown up all over the screen, inviting a Buñuelian razor which he, in his gentility, forbears to proffer. The writer stands here at the bottom of Mr Haines's private staircase and stares out at the church. Maybe he was imagining a bizarre scenario. Maybe he was fantasising that late one night a white figure, lit by candlelight, appears on the church's organ loft. And that Mr Haines, bathed in moonlight behind the gravestones, knife drawn, sees it through the red filter of the stained glass. And then the figure flings its arms into the air and vanishes. And Mr Haines smiles. For it is only old Mrs Dangerfield, plummeting once more to her death. And perhaps somewhere in the trees an owl hoots – or perhaps it is the bleating of a goat?

Ah, Herr Wolf has fallen silent. Somewhere, no doubt, a bomb is exploding or a machine gun rattling or a knife being drawn against a throat.

Stevenson hints at the possibility that the writer rises from his bed at night, at the instigation of a personal ghost. I raised this with Stevenson and he mentioned two nights in particular when he had observed such an occurrence. On one occasion, apparently, the writer was found, wrapped in a blanket, attempting to bed down with the cockroaches in Henri's kitchen – and was quietly escorted back to his own accommodation.

The second took place on the very night that now concerns us – the night of his abduction. An hour after midnight he was found, fully clothed, outside that dark granite building surmounted by a stone ball – the ballroom. In the old days the Earls, their guests and their ladies would whirl around inside here to the music of an orchestra, while coaches waited outside and a train of servants ferried food and wine from the Hall.

The writer was sitting, fully clothed and cross-legged on the ground, staring up at the ballroom's large wooden door, eyes fixed on the thick iron ring that lifts the latch on the other side. His appearance here at this time was a potential problem as Mr Haines was already inside the ballroom, examining the coverage from his cameras, in preparation for the night's events. Stevenson moved silently up behind the writer and gently lifted him to his feet. They walked slowly back to the Hall, Stevenson's hand supporting the writer's elbow. The silence was broken only once, as they walked up the steps to the north entrance. The writer said, 'Is it time to go home?' and Stevenson replied, 'Nearly, sir.' Back upstairs the writer climbed into bed like a child and slept again. For an hour. It was useful, when they came for him, that he was wearing all his clothes. Have you ever tried to dress a corpse?

One could, of course, argue that the writer sleepwalked

through his whole time at the Hall!

Stevenson's note. It was hoped that he could be dissuaded from writing it, but it was not to be. He truly is a good man.

Ah, the writer's pathetic hopes for a new morning that he will never see. These lines bring a tear to my eye every time I read them.

Well then, it falls to me to finish this story, as best I can. I have relied in this on the evidence gathered by Mr Haines's extensive network of cameras. Bryan Forbes extols the use of 'secret cameras' when filming events from a distance. In *Seance on a Wet Afternoon* one was stationed between the neon lights on top of the Warners cinema in London's Leicester Square. From here Mr Forbes filmed Billy's attempts to contact the kidnapped girl's father.

In what follows I have done my best to present events from the writer's perspective – what an old softie I am. But I have tried, too, to use a little imagination. As I am an editor, this might perhaps be regarded as not being my forte. But editing is not all I do, so, who knows, maybe I have done all right. OK, let's go.

The writer left the Hall at 11.23 p.m., stumbling slightly as he negotiated the steps in the dark. He was wearing a baggy sweatshirt and loose-fitting corduroy trousers. He had a scarf loosely tied around his neck – the kind your mother might knit you. The music he had heard in his room began to get a little louder as he travelled along the north side of the Hall and turned left along the road where he had encountered the security guard the day before. As he walked, though, it became clear that what he was hearing was not 'fairground music' but an orchestral version of Mr Haines's record *After Murder Park*. Good to know that those years at the London College of Music were not wasted, after all.

Had Mr Haines, using the mediumistic powers we all suspect him of having, discovered the meaning behind the writer's sister's death? Was he leading him towards the personal enlightenment he so much craved? Far off, in the woods ahead of him, the writer saw a white light shining. He headed towards it.

As the writer came closer, he saw that there were other lights, further off. As he came closer still, he realised that on the other side of the trees that still obscured his vision, there was actually a large, open space, lit by a whole host of lights. Before reaching out to that final destination, though, he paused briefly to write on a piece of paper, which he then shoved into his pocket.

A minute or two later, he stood on the edge of the trees. And found himself staring up at a rusting metal archway, pitted with barbed wire, above which, etched against a sky with clouds racing across a full moon, were the words 'Murder Park'.

As he walked through the arch into the partly-reclaimed scrubland, lit by lights hung on gantries, on overhead wires and on trees shorn of their lower branches, he heard the sound of a woman crying in the distance. At this point he turned to look back the way he had come. I believe he thought about returning to the Hall. But now the security guard he had met the previous day stood behind him, gun presented. And so the writer turned again and continued walking. Above his head the giant balloon figures of the Deverell Twins bobbed against the night sky, jostling each other for position.

There was a footpath ahead of the writer, lit by red Chinese lanterns. He followed it. Nestling in the foliage on either side of him now he saw statues. Lenny and Vanessa were there, embracing each other under a sprig of stone mistletoe. Opposite them was the kid in the lamé jacket, now sporting a sickly grin and a red-stained bullethole through his forehead. Unity Mitford and Gudrun Ensslin faced each other, stone-faced. The first Earl's Beasts proudly presented their huge erect members and the Ancient Journalist cradled Humpty Dumpty in his arms. Here, too, were waxworks of Mr Haines and his imaginary model – the tops of their heads beginning to melt underneath the lanterns, distorting their faces with large drips and tiny waves. Here also were the mannequins in their anti-contamination suits, in terrorist chic and in Nazi uniforms. Somewhere a dog howled. The ghost of Marmaduke, the first

Earl's hound, perhaps, pining across the years for his long-dead master. And then the writer heard a different kind of howling – and a chanting, cackling and caterwauling. And he saw dark shapes cavorting in the woodland behind the statues. The X-Boogie Men pranced and jumped there, their fiery torches lighting up their red eyes. The writer averted his gaze and continued along the footpath. It led to a river. The chants of the X-Boogie Men now became the drunken carousing of the Dead Sea Navigators' old drinking crew – shouts and jeers punctuating an alcohol-sodden rendition of 'You're going home in a fucking ambulance'. The writer followed the river and it led to an old dockside. And there he found a crumbling jetty, a rusting crane and a deserted warehouse. Next to the warehouse was the old dock-keeper's cottage. The crying was much louder now – it was coming from the front room.

The writer walked in but he found that the room was empty – apart from a candle, recently snuffed out, on a table and, next to it, a copy of Charles Dickens's *Oliver Twist*. The writer shouted 'Mum!', 'Jessica! Jessica!' but there was no reply. He walked up the old wooden staircase and searched the damp, crumbling rooms on the first floor, again shouting for his mother and sister. In the bedroom at the front was an unmade bed – it looked as though the sheets and blankets had been cast off in a hurry. But there was no one there. And so he walked back down the stairs.

In the front room once again, he looked through the window, out to the river. A thick fog was rolling across it now. He heard the sound of crying again – and this time he froze. For these were the cries of a child. They seemed to be coming from out on the water. He made for the stairs. On the dockside the actors had gathered: the barman from the saloon in Tombstone, a child bride, the phantom flyer, the girl in the wreckage, the preacher from the cabin of the light aircraft. Their faces flitted in and out of the fog that swirled around them. They stared at the writer – the men's hands in their pockets, the women's at their sides. The phantom flyer was looking up at the sky. The writer began to walk along the jetty. At its far end there was a small wooden platform. As he strode towards it, and then broke into a run, Catherine, the child bride, moved towards the door of the warehouse. Immediately, its walls were flooded with huge colour projections of the Baader-Meinhof suicides – a bearded Holger Meins, Gudrun Ensslin and Ulrike Meinhof as blondes, Andreas Baader in dark glasses, a moustachioed Jan-Carl Raspe. Superimposed over these images was the grey outline of a giant swastika. The writer seemed not to see any of this. As he ran towards the water's edge, he tore off his sweatshirt. Catherine began to run towards him. The writer leapt into the water. By the time Catherine reached the river bank, he was lost in the fog. She crouched down on the wooden boards and stared through the grey mist after him. And then she untied the small rowing boat moored there, climbed in, and began to move across the water.

It seems that the writer had made one last attempt to communicate with the world. In the front room of the dock-keeper's cottage was found that brief, hastily scribbled note, its script careering across the page, that he had written on the very edge of Murder Park, under a moon obscured by scudding clouds.

The note said:

'I hear what you say, Stevenson, but I'm not like you.

If you thought I was then I am sorry. I wish I could have called you 'friend'.

Goodbye.'

And so we leave the writer. Maybe he has found his destiny out on the water? Maybe Jessica was waiting for him there? A Deverell girl, calling to him across the years.

And so to the loose ends.

There may be a small collection of unanswered email for the writer on Mr Haines's server. Sadly, Stevenson was unable to solve the mystery of the malfunctioning internet connection until it was too late. Some messages got through but others, it seems, never made it. Maybe there were emails there from Fiona. There was a little more about her in the writer's book.

Obviously I deleted it – we couldn't have it interfering with our story. But having brought up her name – and now that the story is over – let me see if I can remember any of it...

Ah yes, she had wanted to move in with him, he says. But he, of course, had decided upon his solitary life. And so he refused her. There was a certain amount of soul searching from the writer then as he pondered again the sagacity of this decision. At the end of all this came the rather startling admission that he had been unable to live with any girlfriend – not that there had been many – since leaving home, or even to have them round to his place on a regular basis. After a while, you see, as they sat on the sofa in the evenings, he would turn to them and see his sister. And when they brought him his food, the face that he saw, smiling down at him, would be hers. And when he woke in the morning and opened his eyes, his sister would be asleep next to him. Every girl that he brought back home with him eventually acquired Jessica's face. But with Fiona it had taken longer. Whole months went by and all he saw was Fiona's face. He dared to hope. And then came the day when he had to confront the water with her. A weekend at the seaside. Walking down through the town. Hot, sunny, crowded, noisy – the perfect antithesis to that morning, so long ago, down at the boating lake. They laid out their towels on the sand and walked hand in hand towards the sea. He turned towards her – and saw Jessica. He let go of her hand. She saw the horror in his face and knew what had happened. They sat on the beach for a while, not talking. And then they packed up their things and walked back to the car. And they returned home. But his home was hers no longer. The writer was on his own again. And this time for good.

But what did he find at the end of this last long night? Did he really find his sister? Or maybe the writer has done a Lord Lucan – committed his crime and vanished to a better place? Perhaps he has gone in search of Mr Haines's soul. Or was the impact of his dive into the water enough to rouse him from his waking dream and to lay to rest once and for all Jessica's ghost? Did he, despite everything, find his taxi waiting in front of the steps, engine running?

But enough of the writer, I hear you say. What of our real subject? What of Mr Haines?

Indeed. Well, the Auteur has become an auteur.

I have watched Mr Haines's film. It is a magnificent achievement. I shall give you an idea of it, but do not worry, this will not spoil it for you – after all, you already know the plot. Shot largely in secret, it presents the fascinating story told by his songs, as witnessed and lived by the writer. In this it forms a highly efficacious antidote to that most justly derided of modern forms, the reality TV show.

At the beginning of the film, once the writer is safely within the North Hall and in the care of Stevenson, the camera pans to a shot of the windows in the east wing where Mr Haines has his quarters. In an homage to *Seance on a Wet Afternoon*, the image distorts as rain falls upon the lens.

We look on as the writer watches the various presentations of Mr Haines's works. We see him gradually become more involved in them. Cut with these sequences are reshootings of the songs' original scenarios, filmed after the writer's disappearance, in which the actors are given room to breathe, scenery to inhabit, props to own and outfits to die for. Here, the grounds and temples, arches, bridges, river, gardens and lakes are exploited to the full. It is a most sumptuous employment of this place's resources. In these scenes the cameras, set free from their clandestine coverage, pan and zoom, soar and plummet, and cut between one another with abandon.

Some scenes in the original footage, however, could not be improved upon and needed no further comment from Mr Haines. They have not been reshot – they remain entire and uninterrupted. The performance by Mr Haines in the Temple of Hope is one such. Look at the writer's face here during the appearance of the ghosts. Artificially created fear, no matter how accomplished the actor responding to it, can never compete with the real thing.

Some of the material shot using the camera hidden in the writer's quarters is rather poignant. Whether falling asleep in the bath or bent over his computer, struggling for the right words, or curled up tight in his bed, eyes open wide in the infra red light, there is an ever-present air of inevitable tragedy that adds a nice pathos to the film.

When the writer arrives in the woods of Murder Park we see the trees as they are presented in the climax to Mr Forbes's *Seance* – as if we are lying on our side on the ground. Slowly our view stabilises as we get to our feet. And then a little prophetic fog swirls. The events on the dockside are embellished by shots from high up on the crane, from the roof of the dock-keeper's cottage, from a boat moored on the river and from an underwater camera which records the writer's entry into the water. The film's final sequence, again recalling *Seance on a Wet Afternoon*, begins with a haunting close-up of the ripples on the lake, which gradually fade to nothing as the credits play. Fog hangs over the water, but gradually disperses as the ripples grow smooth. In the end there is nothing but untroubled water and a starry night. And then we cut to a shot of the Hall. It is seen upside down, reflected in a puddle. Successive drops of rain blur the image, but it stabilises after each one before finally holding.

Miss Françoise, too, is very pleased with Mr Haines's film – and that is important, for it is she who commissioned it.

James Jefferson Griff IV met her and Catherine one evening in an exclusive wine bar tucked behind London's Park Lane. The two young ladies were sitting on tall bar stools, high heels dangling from their long, elegant legs. JJ was immediately taken with them. They responded sweetly to the statements he made about his wealth, property and influence, and accepted his invitation to spend a weekend at the Hall. The weekend became a week and the week became a month. And then the month multiplied. It was Miss Françoise who found that she could do most in the way of ministering to JJ's needs and it was she who, within a year, had taken the highest place in his affections. It was she, too, who nursed him faithfully through his final illness. And, when the old chap's time finally ran out and he was laid to rest, it was she to whom the Hall was left in his will. Miss Françoise is a great admirer of Mr Haines's work. She decided to provide him with the means to put together a cinematic account of it. To the public a story would be told of Mr Haines meeting a showgirl in Las Vegas and marrying her, of discovering her to be rich and landed, of acquiring through this marriage an aristocratic English estate. Catherine was more than happy to play the part of this fictitious young lady. The story worked. It brought the interest of the media – and it brought the writer. Miss Françoise told Mr Haines that he would be free to make his film in any way he saw fit. For six months he would be in sole charge of the Hall. It would become his, to do with what he willed. 'Take it over,' she said. 'Make it yours. Own it. Become it and let it become you.' We are indebted to Miss Françoise for her generosity and commitment.

Now that Mr Haines's work at the Hall is done, now that his film is complete, he will take his leave of this rarefied world and return to the metropolis. Here he will pick up his guitar once more. The Hall was fun – but it is over.

And what of Stevenson? What will become of him? He, too, will leave the Hall. He will move on. And he will continue to move on until his work is done. He will pursue his dedication to his cause until the end.

After the final reflected image of the Hall in Mr Haines's film, the camera moves across the lawn, rises to greet the Hall itself and then moves in through the open window of the State Drawing Room. Here we see Mr Haines sitting on a Louis XV commode, a gold Gibson SG across his lap. Above him is a canopy spread by Time and supported by Zephyrs. We hear his song 'Future Generation' play while he stares at the camera. As the song comes to a close, his head turns towards the window and a smile spreads across his face. And then the credits begin to roll.

Cast list of Mr Haines's film:

First actor: Circus father, Rick, Paul, Preacher, Man in saloon, Chuck, Ed, Joe, The neo-fascist, Hitler, Edward VIII, Cameraman at Mr Haines's performance, Terrorist.

Second actor: Circus son, James, Barman, Jim, Semi-detached husband, Oswald Mosley, Doctor, Security guard, Terrorist.

The actor resembling Mr Haines: Harry, Pilot, Horseback drinker, Mr Haines, 'A Matter of Life and Death' airman, George V, Terrorist.

Catherine: Circus mother, Rita, Joanna, Child Bride 1, Hotel victim, Girl in bed, Ra-ra girl, New Romantic, Sunday girl, Mother of terrorist girl, Teacher, Ideal home woman, Deverells girl, Beach girl, Unity Mitford, Wallis Simpson, Terrorist, Girl at dockside.

Françoise: Margaret, Child Bride 2, Edith, Girl in the wreckage, 'New baby' girl, Semi-detached wife, Schoolgirl, New Queen of the South, Diana Mitford, Terrorist.

Mary: Woman in saloon, Nurse, Terrorist.

The son of the actor resembling Mr Haines: The Kid.

The daughter of the actor resembling Mr Haines: The little girl in the bedroom.

Stevenson: Taxi driver, The Killer, Aleister Crowley, Andreas.

Mr Haines: Himself.

Acknowledgements

Thanks to Luke Haines for agreeing to be interviewed, for having no objections to the book, and for allowing me to make dramatic use of the scenarios from his songs. Thanks to both him and John Moore for their permission to make dramatic use of the scenarios from the songs they co-wrote for Black Box Recorder.

Thanks to George Galbraith for all his support and hard work in getting this into print and to Simon Smith, Juno Baker and Marko Stamenkovic for their help.

Thanks for online research materials to:

The Luke Haines Resource, Stephen Rushe, Adam Leonard, Tobias Johansson.

Unless stated below, all quotations from the editor's conversations with Luke Haines come from interviews between Mr Haines and the author:

p 65 *Vox* Max Bell June 1994
p 81 *Kid's Issue* Daniel Patrick Quinn, no.4
p 220 *terapijanet* Pedja August 2005 www.terapija.net

Other quotations:

pp 51, 219 'The Case of Charles Dexter Ward' HP Lovecraft
p 57 *Jerusalem: The Emanation of the Giant Albion* William Blake
p 62 Untitled poem William Blake
pp 64,196 *The Gentle Art of Making Enemies* James Abbott McNeill Whistler
The little girl's conversation with Stevenson on pp 116-118 is based on material included in a remix of 'The Facts of Life' by The Chocolate Layers.

Other works referred to:

England is Mine Michael Bracewell HarperCollins London 1997

Satan Wants Me Robert Irwin Dedalus Sawtry 1999

Seance on (a) Wet Afternoon: Final Revised Screenplay Bryan Forbes

The English: A Portrait of a People Jeremy Paxman Michael Joseph London 1998

Selected discography

Singles/EPs

The Auteurs -   Showgirl/Glad to be Gone/Staying Power
                (1993)

The Auteurs -   How Could I be Wrong/High Diving Horses/
                Wedding Day/Staying Power (1993)

The Auteurs -   Housebreaker/Valet Parking (1993)

The Auteurs -   New French Girlfriend/Lenny Valentino (1993)

The Auteurs -   Lenny Valentino/Car Crazy/Vacant Lot/
                Lenny Valentino (1993)

                Lenny Valentino/Disney World (7")

The Auteurs -   Chinese Bakery/Government Bookstore/
                Everything You Say Will Destroy You (1994)

                Chinese Bakery/Modern History/
                Chinese Bakery

Baader Meinhof - Baader Meinhof/Meet Me at the Airport (1995)

The Auteurs -   Back with the Killer EP:
                Unsolved Child Murder/
                Back with the Killer Again/Former Fan/
                Kenneth Anger's Bad Dream (1995)

The Auteurs -   Light Aircraft on Fire EP:
                Light Aircraft on Fire/Buddha/Car Crash/
                X-Boogie Man (1996)

The Auteurs -   Kids Issue EP:
                Kids Issue/Buddha/A New Life a New Family/
                After Murder Park (1996)

Black Box
Recorder -   Child Psychology/Girl Singing in the Wreckage/
                Seasons in the Sun (1998)

Black Box
Recorder -   England Made Me/Factory Radio/
                Child Psychology (video) (1998)

                England Made Me/Lord Lucan is Missing (7")

The Auteurs -   The Rubettes/Breaking Up/
                Get Wrecked at Home (1999)

Black Box
Recorder -   The Facts of Life/Soul Boy/
                Start as You Mean to go on (2000)

                The Facts of Life/Brutality/
                Watch the Angel, Not the Wire

Black Box
Recorder -   The Art of Driving/The Facts of Life/
                Rock'N'Roll Suicide (2000)

                The Art of Driving/Uptown Top Ranking/
                The Facts of Life

Black Box
Recorder -   These are the Things/Seventeen and Deadly/
                Land of Our Fathers (2003)

Black Box
Recorder -   The School Song/Passionoia/
                Lord Lucan is Missing (2003)

Luke Haines -   Off My Rocker at the Art School Bop/
                I am the Best Artist/Skinny White Girls (2006)

                Off My Rocker at the Art School Bop/
                I am the Best Artist/Skinny White Girls/
                Art School Acoustic (iTunes)

Luke Haines -   Leeds United EP:
                Leeds United/Bovver Boys/Country Life/Queen
                Elizabeth/Leeds United (2007)

Black Arts (Black Box Recorder/Art Brut) -
                Christmas Number One/Glam Casual (2007)

Albums

The Auteurs - *New Wave* (1993)
The Auteurs - *Now I'm a Cowboy* (1994)
The Auteurs - *After Murder Park* (1996)
Baader Meinhof - *Baader Meinhof* (1996)
Black Box Recorder - *England Made Me* (1998)
The Auteurs - *How I Learned to Love The Bootboys* (1999)
Black Box Recorder - *The Facts of Life* (2000)
Black Box Recorder - *The Worst of Black Box Recorder* (2001) (USA)
Luke Haines - *Christie Malry's Own Double Entry*. OST (2001)
Luke Haines - *The Oliver Twist Manifesto* (2001)
Black Box Recorder - *Passionoia* (2003)
Luke Haines – *Das Capital* (2003)
Auteurs, Baader Meinhof, Luke Haines - *Luke Haines is Dead* (2005)
Luke Haines - *Off My Rocker at the Art School Bop* (2006)